Mathematics C

PEOPLES Common Core

From the publisher of 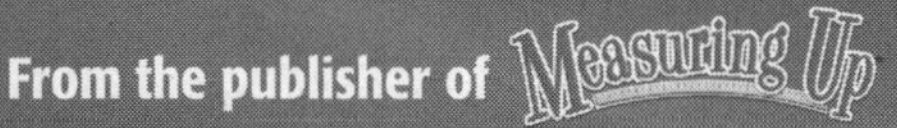

peopleseducation.com

Peoples Education
Your partner in student success

Executive Vice President, Chief Creative Officer: Diane Miller
Editorial Development: Publisher's Partnership
Managing Editor: Kerri Gero
Editorial Assistant: Amy Priddy Wierzbicki
Copy Editor: Katy Leclercq
Vice President of Marketing: Victoria Ameer Kiely
Senior Marketing Manager: Christine Grasso
Marketing Manager: Victoria Leo
Production Director: Jason Grasso
Production Manager: Jennifer Bridges Brewer
Assistant Production Managers: Steven Genzano, Jennifer Tully
Director of Permissions: Kristine Liebman
Cover Design: Joe Guerrero, Todd Kochakji

Peoples Education, Inc.
299 Market Street
Saddle Brook, New Jersey 07663

ISBN 978-1-61734-663-7

Manufactured in Newburyport, MA in January 2012 by BRADFORD & BIGELOW, INC.

Printed in the United States of America.

10 9 8 7 6 5 4 3

Table of Contents

Your teacher may choose to assign the pretest to diagnose your CCSS proficiency and direct you to help in this worktext.

Chapter 1: Operations & Algebraic Thinking

CHAPTER 4 Measurement & Data

CHAPTER 5 Geometry

Your teacher may choose to assign the posttest for this program to check your learning.

Practice Path
Check out our Common Core web-based programs for access to thousands of additional practice items.

Grade 3 Common Core State Standards Overview

Operations and Algebraic Thinking

- Represent and solve problems involving multiplication and division.
- Understand properties of multiplication and the relationship between multiplication and division.
- Multiply and divide within 100.
- Solve problems involving the four operations, and identify and explain patterns in arithmetic.

Number and Operations in Base Ten

- Use place value understanding and properties of operations to perform multi-digit arithmetic.

Number and Operations—Fractions

- Develop understanding of fractions as numbers.

Measurement and Data

- Solve problems involving measurement and estimation of intervals of time, liquid volumes, and masses of objects.
- Represent and interpret data.
- Geometric measurement: understand concepts of area and relate area to multiplication and to addition.
- Geometric measurement: recognize perimeter as an attribute of plane figures and distinguish between linear and area measures.

Geometry

- Reason with shapes and their attributes.

Mathematical Practices

1. Make sense of problems and persevere in solving them.
2. Reason abstractly and quantitatively.
3. Construct viable arguments and critique the reasoning of others.
4. Model with mathematics.
5. Use appropriate tools strategically.
6. Attend to precision.
7. Look for and make use of structure.
8. Look for and express regularity in repeated reasoning.

Correlation to the Common Core State Standards

This worktext is customized to the Common Core State Standards for Mathematics. Most lessons focus on one content standard for in-depth review. Mathematical Practices are interwoven throughout each lesson to connect practices to content at point-of-use and promote depth of understanding.

Common Core State Standards	Lessons
Mathematical Practices	
1. Make sense of problems and persevere in solving them.	embedded throughout
2. Reason abstractly and quantitatively.	embedded throughout
3. Construct viable arguments and critique the reasoning of others.	embedded throughout
4. Model with mathematics.	embedded throughout
5. Use appropriate tools strategically.	embedded throughout
6. Attend to precision.	embedded throughout
7. Look for and make use of structure.	embedded throughout
8. Look for and express regularity in repeated reasoning.	embedded throughout
3.OA Operations and Algebraic Thinking	
Represent and solve problems involving multiplication and division.	
1. Interpret products of whole numbers, e.g., interpret 5×7 as the total number of objects in 5 groups of 7 objects each. *For example, describe a context in which a total number of objects can be expressed as* 5×7.	1
2. Interpret whole-number quotients of whole numbers, e.g., interpret $56 \div 8$ as the number of objects in each share when 56 objects are partitioned equally into 8 shares, or as a number of shares when 56 objects are partitioned into equal shares of 8 objects each. *For example, describe a context in which a number of shares or a number of groups can be expressed as* $56 \div 8$.	2
3. Use multiplication and division within 100 to solve word problems in situations involving equal groups, arrays, and measurement quantities, e.g., by using drawings and equations with a symbol for the unknown number to represent the problem.[1]	3, 4
4. Determine the unknown whole number in a multiplication or division equation relating three whole numbers. *For example, determine the unknown number that makes the equation true in each of the equations* $8 \times ? = 48$, $5 = \_ \div 3$, $6 \times 6 = ?$	5

Common Core State Standards	Lessons
Understand properties of multiplication and the relationship between multiplication and division.	
5. Apply properties of operations as strategies to multiply and divide.[2] *Examples: If $6 \times 4 = 24$ is known, then $4 \times 6 = 24$ is also known. (Commutative property of multiplication.) $3 \times 5 \times 2$ can be found by $3 \times 5 = 15$, then $15 \times 2 = 30$, or by $5 \times 2 = 10$, then $3 \times 10 = 30$. (Associative property of multiplication.) Knowing that $8 \times 5 = 40$ and $8 \times 2 = 16$, one can find 8×7 as $8 \times (5 + 2) = (8 \times 5) + (8 \times 2) = 40 + 16 = 56$. (Distributive property.)*	6
6. Understand division as an unknown-factor problem. *For example, find $32 \div 8$ by finding the number that makes 32 when multiplied by 8.*	7
Multiply and divide within 100.	
7. Fluently multiply and divide within 100, using strategies such as the relationship between multiplication and division (e.g., knowing that $8 \times 5 = 40$, one knows $40 \div 5 = 8$) or properties of operations. By the end of Grade 3, know from memory all products of two one-digit numbers.	8
8. Solve two-step word problems using the four operations. Represent these problems using equations with a letter standing for the unknown quantity. Assess the reasonableness of answers using mental computation and estimation strategies including rounding.[3]	9
9. Identify arithmetic patterns (including patterns in the addition table or multiplication table), and explain them using properties of operations. *For example, observe that 4 times a number is always even, and explain why 4 times a number can be decomposed into two equal addends.*	10
3.NBT Number and Operations in Base Ten	
Use place value understanding and properties of operations to perform multi-digit arithmetic.	
1. Use place value understanding to round whole numbers to the nearest 10 or 100.	11
2. Fluently add and subtract within 1000 using strategies and algorithms based on place value, properties of operations, and/or the relationship between addition and subtraction.	12, 13, 14
3. Multiply one-digit whole numbers by multiples of 10 in the range 10–90 (e.g., 9×80, 5×60) using strategies based on place value and properties of operations.	15
3.NF Number and Operations-Fractions	
Develop understanding of fractions as numbers.	
1. Understand a fraction $\frac{1}{b}$ as the quantity formed by 1 part when a whole is partitioned into b equal parts; understand a fraction $\frac{a}{b}$ as the quantity formed by a parts of size $\frac{1}{b}$.	16
2. Understand a fraction as a number on the number line; represent fractions on a number line diagram.	17, 18
a. Represent a fraction $\frac{1}{b}$ on a number line diagram by defining the interval from 0 to 1 as the whole and partitioning it into b equal parts. Recognize that each part has size $\frac{1}{b}$ and that the endpoint of the part based at 0 locates the number $\frac{1}{b}$ on the number line.	17
b. Represent a fraction $\frac{a}{b}$ on a number line diagram by marking off a lengths $\frac{1}{b}$ from 0. Recognize that the resulting interval has size $\frac{a}{b}$ and that its endpoint locates the number $\frac{a}{b}$ on the number line.	18
3. Explain equivalence of fractions in special cases, and compare fractions by reasoning about their size.	19, 20, 21, 22
a. Understand two fractions as equivalent (equal) if they are the same size, or the same point on a number line.	19

Common Core State Standards	Lessons
b. Recognize and generate simple equivalent fractions, e.g., $\frac{1}{2} = \frac{2}{4}$, $\frac{4}{6} = \frac{2}{3}$). Explain why the fractions are equivalent, e.g., by using a visual fraction model.	20
c. Express whole numbers as fractions, and recognize fractions that are equivalent to whole numbers. *Examples: Express 3 in the form* $3 = \frac{3}{1}$; *recognize that* $\frac{6}{1} = 6$; *locate* $\frac{4}{4}$ *and 1 at the same point of a number line diagram.*	21
d. Compare two fractions with the same numerator or the same denominator by reasoning about their size. Recognize that comparisons are valid only when the two fractions refer to the same whole. Record the results of comparisons with the symbols >, =, or <, and justify the conclusions, e.g., by using a visual fraction model.	22
3.MD Measurement and Data	
Solve problems involving measurement and estimation of intervals of time, liquid volumes, and masses of objects.	
1. Tell and write time to the nearest minute and measure time intervals in minutes. Solve word problems involving addition and subtraction of time intervals in minutes, e.g., by representing the problem on a number line diagram.	23
2. Measure and estimate liquid volumes and masses of objects using standard units of grams (g), kilograms (kg), and liters (l). Add, subtract, multiply, or divide to solve one-step word problems involving masses or volumes that are given in the same units, e.g., by using drawings (such as a beaker with a measurement scale) to represent the problem.	24, 25
Represent and interpret data.	
3. Draw a scaled picture graph and a scaled bar graph to represent a data set with several categories. Solve one- and two-step "how many more" and "how many less" problems using information presented in scaled bar graphs. *For example, draw a bar graph in which each square in the bar graph might represent 5 pets.*	26, 27
4. Generate measurement data by measuring lengths using rulers marked with halves and fourths of an inch. Show the data by making a line plot, where the horizontal scale is marked off in appropriate units— whole numbers, halves, or quarters.	28, 29
Geometric measurement: understand concepts of area and relate area to multiplication and to addition.	
5. Recognize area as an attribute of plane figures and understand concepts of area measurement.	30
a. A square with side length 1 unit, called "a unit square," is said to have "one square unit" of area, and can be used to measure area.	30
b. A plane figure which can be covered without gaps or overlaps by *n* unit squares is said to have an area of *n* square units.	30
6. Measure areas by counting unit squares (square cm, square m, square in, square ft, and improvised units).	31
7. Relate area to the operations of multiplication and addition.	32, 33, 34, 35
a. Find the area of a rectangle with whole-number side lengths by tiling it, and show that the area is the same as would be found by multiplying the side lengths.	32
b. Multiply side lengths to find areas of rectangles with whole-number side lengths in the context of solving real world and mathematical problems, and represent whole-number products as rectangular areas in mathematical reasoning.	33

Common Core State Standards	Lessons
c. Use tiling to show in a concrete case that the area of a rectangle with whole-number side lengths a and $b + c$ is the sum of $a \times b$ and $a \times c$. Use area models to represent the distributive property in mathematical reasoning.	34
d. Recognize area as additive. Find areas of rectilinear figures by decomposing them into non-overlapping rectangles and adding the areas of the non-overlapping parts, applying this technique to solve real world problems.	35
Geometric measurement: recognize perimeter as an attribute of plane figures and distinguish between linear and area measures.	
8. Solve real world and mathematical problems involving perimeters of polygons, including finding the perimeter given the side lengths, finding an unknown side length, and exhibiting rectangles with the same perimeter and different areas or with the same area and different perimeters.	36, 37
3.G Geometry	
Reason with shapes and their attributes.	
1. Understand that shapes in different categories (e.g., rhombuses, rectangles, and others) may share attributes (e.g., having four sides), and that the shared attributes can define a larger category (e.g., quadrilaterals). Recognize rhombuses, rectangles, and squares as examples of quadrilaterals, and draw examples of quadrilaterals that do not belong to any of these subcategories.	38, 39
2. Partition shapes into parts with equal areas. Express the area of each part as a unit fraction of the whole. *For example, partition a shape into 4 parts with equal area, and describe the area of each part as $\frac{1}{4}$ of the area of the shape.*	40

To the Student:

It's never too soon to prepare for your future. The same goes for learning the new Common Core State Standards for your grade level. This new set of expectations will help you be prepared for college and your career, and to be successful in all your academic pursuits.

The lessons in this book are geared toward helping you master all the Common Core State Standards for mathematics in a structured way.

Peoples Common Core has 5 chapters, each one is focused on a different set of skills and modeled on the Common Core State Standards.

Each chapter includes:

- A brief review of skills and key vocabulary
- Suggested tools to help you learn
- Real world examples
- Step-by-step problem-solving instruction
- A variety of activities and questions that allow you to show your learning
- Multiple-choice, short-answer, and extended-response question practice
- A special Kick It Up project and activity to boost your learning to the next level

These lessons will help you build your mathematics skills and improve your high-level thinking. The lessons may seem challenging at first, but keep at it and you will be a success!

Have a great school year!

To Parents and Families:

Peoples Education has created this Common Core book to help your child master the new Common Core State Standards, and to get your child to think on a higher level. The Common Core State Standards are a clear set of K–12 grade-specific expectations. Developed by a consortium of states and coordinated by the National Governors Association and the Council of Chief State School Officers, these standards define what it means for students to be college- and career-ready in the 21st century. As your child moves through this book, encourage your child to consider, analyze, interpret, and evaluate instead of just recalling simple facts.

Each of the 5 chapters in this book is focused on a different set of skills, modeled on the Common Core State Standards.

Each chapter includes:

- A review of skills and key vocabulary
- Real world examples
- Step-by-step problem-solving instruction
- A variety of activities and questions that allow your child to show his or her skill comprehension
- Multiple-choice, short-answer, and extended-response question practice
- A special Kick It Up project and activity to boost your child's learning to the next level

For success in school and the real world, your child needs a solid mathematics foundation, and your involvement is crucial to that success. Here are some suggestions:

Show that mathematics is important, by including your child in activities that require mathematical thinking.

Help find appropriate Internet sites for mathematics. Note how mathematics is used when you are out with your family. Discuss how mathematics is used in financial and banking matters, in careers such as engineering, architecture, and medicine, in space exploration, and in other real-life situations.

Encourage your child to take time to review and check his or her homework. Just solving a problem is not enough. Ask your child whether the answer is reasonable and have him or her explain what led to that answer.

Get involved! Work with us this year to ensure your child's success. Mathematics skills are an essential part of college and career readiness and the real world.

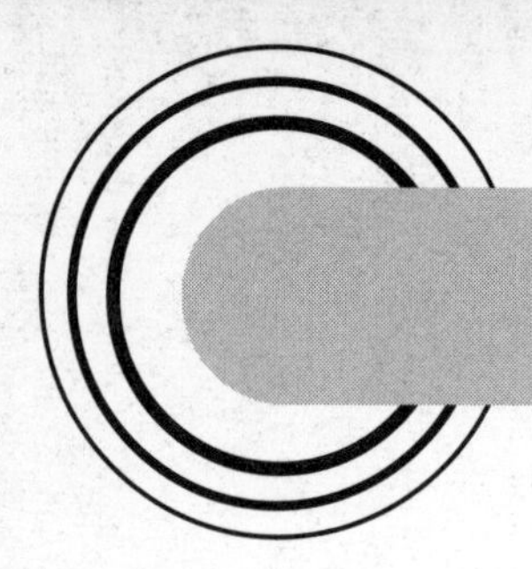

What's Inside

Lessons in this worktext provide instruction, activities, and review for each skill in the Common Core State Standards.

Real World Connections helps you understand the skill with examples and problems from real life. Toolbox lists supplies needed for the lesson, and Key Words highlight the words you will need to know.

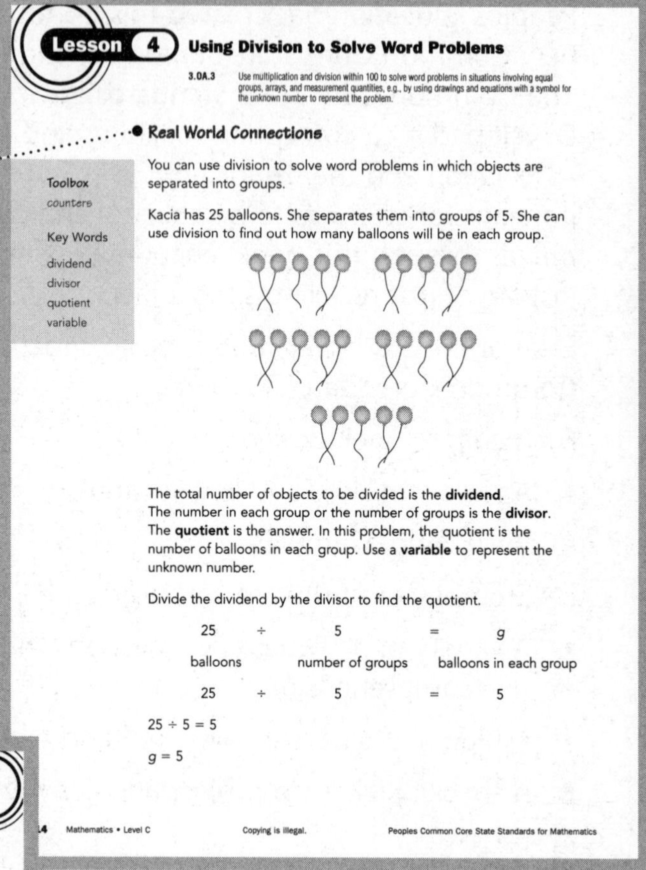

Lesson 4 **Using Division to Solve Word Problems**

3.OA.3 Use multiplication and division within 100 to solve word problems in situations involving equal groups, arrays, and measurement quantities, e.g., by using drawings and equations with a symbol for the unknown number to represent the problem.

Real World Connections

Toolbox
counters

Key Words
dividend
divisor
quotient
variable

You can use division to solve word problems in which objects are separated into groups.

Kacia has 25 balloons. She separates them into groups of 5. She can use division to find out how many balloons will be in each group.

The total number of objects to be divided is the **dividend**. The number in each group or the number of groups is the **divisor**. The **quotient** is the answer. In this problem, the quotient is the number of balloons in each group. Use a **variable** to represent the unknown number.

Divide the dividend by the divisor to find the quotient.

25	÷	5	=	g
balloons		number of groups		balloons in each group
25	÷	5	=	5

$25 \div 5 = 5$

$g = 5$

14 Mathematics • Level C Copying is illegal. Peoples Common Core State Standards for Mathematics

Using Division to Solve Word Problems **4 Lesson**

Take It Apart

Follow these steps to solve a word problem using division.

Step 1 Read the problem carefully. What information are you given?

Step 2 Decide what you need to find out.

Step 3 Write a division sentence with a variable for the unknown number.

Step 4 Divide to solve. Does your answer make sense?

Eric has 15 coins. He separates them into 3 equal groups. How many coins are in each group?

What information are you given?

- how many coins Eric has
- how many groups he separates the coins into

These are the dividend and the divisor.

What do you need to find out?

- how many coins are in each group

This is the quotient.

$15 \div 3 = c$

$15 \div 3 = 5$, so there are 5 coins in each group.

Solve each problem. Use counters if you need help.

1. Carlie wants to give each of her 4 friends the same number of stickers. She has 20 stickers. How many stickers will each friend get?

   ____

2. Elliot has 42 crayons. He gives 6 crayons to each child. How many children did he give crayons to?

   ____

Peoples Education Copying is illegal. Chapter 1 • Operations & Algebraic Thinking 15

Take It Apart helps you solve a problem step-by-step to build your skills.

Put It Together asks you to apply the skill with different types of questions and activities.

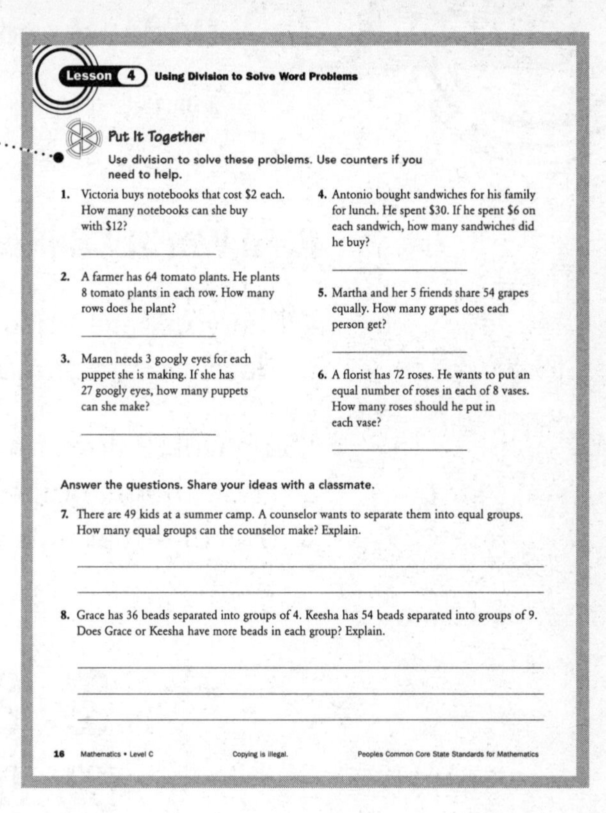

Lesson 4 **Using Division to Solve Word Problems**

Put It Together

Use division to solve these problems. Use counters if you need to help.

1. Victoria buys notebooks that cost $2 each. How many notebooks can she buy with $12?
2. A farmer has 64 tomato plants. He plants 8 tomato plants in each row. How many rows does he plant?
3. Maren needs 3 googly eyes for each puppet she is making. If she has 27 googly eyes, how many puppets can she make?
4. Antonio bought sandwiches for his family for lunch. He spent $30. If he spent $6 on each sandwich, how many sandwiches did he buy?
5. Martha and her 5 friends share 54 grapes equally. How many grapes does each person get?
6. A florist has 72 roses. He wants to put an equal number of roses in each of 8 vases. How many roses should he put in each vase?

Answer the questions. Share your ideas with a classmate.

7. There are 49 kids at a summer camp. A counselor wants to separate them into equal groups. How many equal groups can the counselor make? Explain.
8. Grace has 36 beads separated into groups of 4. Keesha has 54 beads separated into groups of 9. Does Grace or Keesha have more beads in each group? Explain.

16 Mathematics • Level C Copying is illegal. Peoples Common Core State Standards for Mathematics

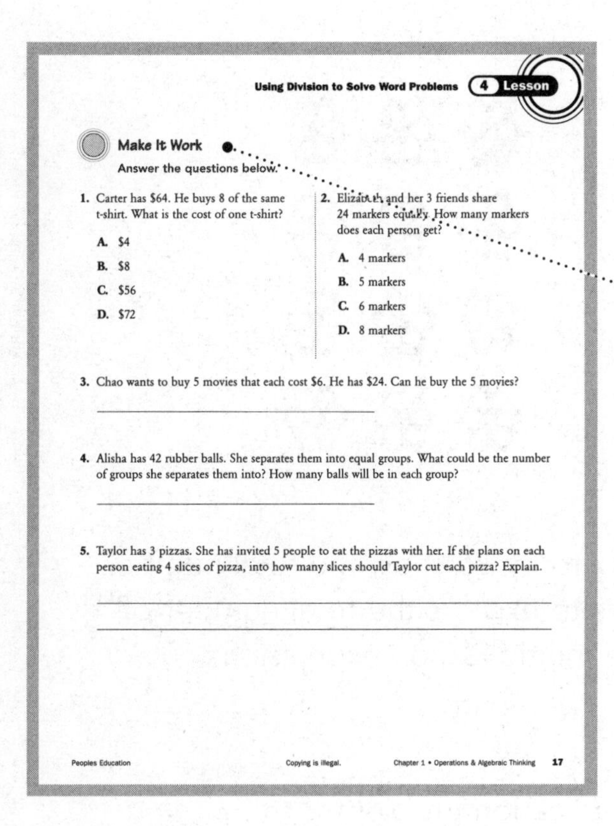

Using Division to Solve Word Problems 4 Lesson

Make It Work

Answer the questions below.

1. Carter has $64. He buys 8 of the same t-shirt. What is the cost of one t-shirt?
   A. $4
   B. $8
   C. $56
   D. $72
2. Elizabeth and her 3 friends share 24 markers equally. How many markers does each person get?
   A. 4 markers
   B. 5 markers
   C. 6 markers
   D. 8 markers
3. Chao wants to buy 5 movies that each cost $6. He has $24. Can he buy the 5 movies?
4. Alisha has 42 rubber balls. She separates them into equal groups. What could be the number of groups she separates them into? How many balls will be in each group?
5. Taylor has 3 pizzas. She has invited 5 people to eat the pizzas with her. If she plans on each person eating 4 slices of pizza, into how many slices should Taylor cut each pizza? Explain.

Peoples Education Copying is illegal. Chapter 1 • Operations & Algebraic Thinking 17

Make It Work assesses your learning on the lesson skill with a variety of formats, including multiple-choice, short-answer, and extended-response questions.

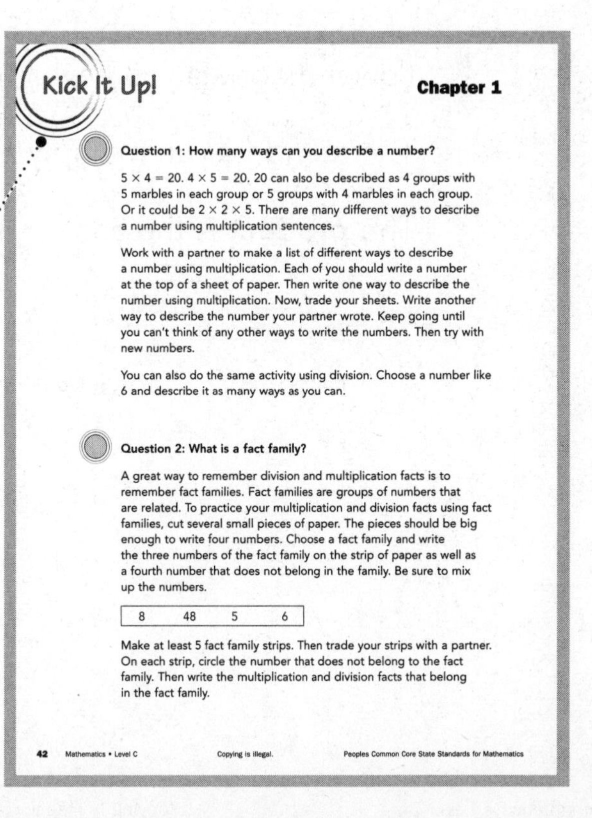

Kick It Up! **Chapter 1**

Question 1: How many ways can you describe a number?

$5 \times 4 = 20$. $4 \times 5 = 20$. 20 can also be described as 4 groups with 5 marbles in each group or 5 groups with 4 marbles in each group. Or it could be $2 \times 2 \times 5$. There are many different ways to describe a number using multiplication sentences.

Work with a partner to make a list of different ways to describe a number using multiplication. Each of you should write a number at the top of a sheet of paper. Then write one way to describe the number using multiplication. Now, trade your sheets. Write another way to describe the number your partner wrote. Keep going until you can't think of any other ways to write the numbers. Then try with new numbers.

You can also do the same activity using division. Choose a number like 6 and describe it as many ways as you can.

Question 2: What is a fact family?

A great way to remember division and multiplication facts is to remember fact families. Fact families are groups of numbers that are related. To practice your multiplication and division facts using fact families, cut several small pieces of paper. The pieces should be big enough to write four numbers. Choose a fact family and write the three numbers of the fact family on the strip of paper as well as a fourth number that does not belong in the family. Be sure to mix up the numbers.

8	48	5	6

Make at least 5 fact family strips. Then trade your strips with a partner. On each strip, circle the number that does not belong to the fact family. Then write the multiplication and division facts that belong in the fact family.

42 Mathematics • Level C Copying is illegal. Peoples Common Core State Standards for Mathematics

Kick It Up end-of-chapter activities are fun projects to build your research, collaboration, problem-solving, technology, and writing skills.

Understanding Multiplication

3.OA.1 Interpret products of whole numbers, e.g., interpret 5 × 7 as the total number of objects in 5 groups of 7 objects each. *For example, describe a context in which a total number of objects can be expressed as 5 × 7.*

Real World Connections

Toolbox

counters

Key Words

factors

product

When you have equal groups of objects, you can use multiplication to describe the number of objects in all.

You have 12 flower magnets on your desk. You notice that you can arrange them in different ways. You can put the 12 magnets into 3 rows of 4 magnets or 4 rows of 3 magnets.

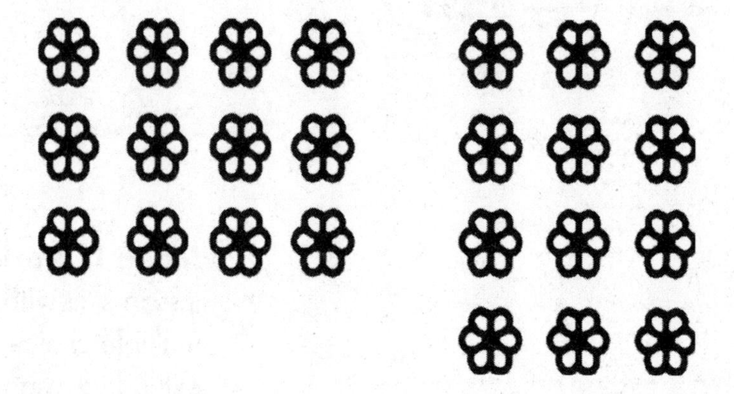

Multiplication is a way to add equal groups to show the total number of objects. 3 × 4 and 4 × 3 are ways to express the total number of flower magnets you have. These are multiplication expressions.

The numbers you multiply are **factors**.

The **product** is the answer in a multiplication problem.

3	×	4	=	12
factor		factor		product

Take It Apart

Follow these steps to show the number of objects in equal groups as a multiplication sentence.

Step 1 Find the number of groups.

Step 2 Find the number of objects in each group.

Step 3 Write a multiplication sentence using the factors.

Multiply to find the product.

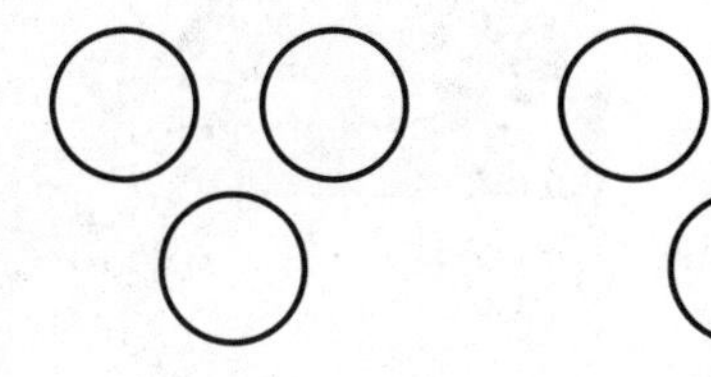

There are 2 groups.

There are 3 objects in each group.

2×3

$2 \times 3 = 6$

Write a multiplication sentence to represent the total number of objects.

1.  

_____ groups × _____ in each group

____

2.    

_____ groups × _____ in each group

____

Put It Together

Use what you know about equal groups and multiplication to write a multiplication sentence. Find the product.

1. ☆☆ ☆☆ ☆☆ ☆☆
☆☆ ☆☆ ☆☆ ☆☆

_____ × _____ = _____

2. 

_____ × _____ = _____

3. ○○ ○○ ○○ ○○ ○○
○○ ○○ ○○ ○○ ○○
○○ ○○ ○○ ○○ ○○

_____ × _____ = _____

4. 

_____ × _____ = _____

Answer the questions. Share your ideas with a classmate.

5. What is another expression you can write to show the number of muffins in question 2?

____

6. Aja has 20 beads. Describe a situation in which she could write the number of beads she has as 4 × 5?

____

____

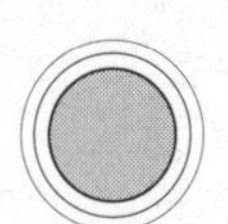

Make It Work

Answer the questions below.

1. Which expression can you use to find the total number of juice boxes?

A. $4 + 3$

B. $3 + 4$

C. $4 - 3$

D. 4×3

2. Which expression describes the total number of peaches?

There are 8 baskets. Each basket has 3 peaches. There are 24 peaches in all.

A. $8 + 3$

B. $8 - 3$

C. 3×3

D. 8×3

3. Ethan has 30 books. He has 6 shelves of books and each shelf has 5 books. Write a multiplication sentence to describe how many books Ethan has.

____

4. Thea put slices of watermelon on plates. She used 7 plates. Each plate has 3 slices. How many slices of watermelon are there?

____

5. Kate has 3 bags of apples. One bag has 5 apples, one bag has 6 apples, and one bag has 7 apples. If she wants to use multiplication to find how many apples she has, what does she need to do first? Explain.

____

____

Understanding Division

3.OA.2 Interpret whole-number quotients of whole numbers, e.g., interpret $56 \div 8$ as the number of objects in each share when 56 objects are partitioned equally into 8 shares, or as a number of shares when 56 objects are partitioned into equal shares of 8 objects each. *For example, describe a context in which a number of shares or a number of groups can be expressed as* $56 \div 8$.

Real World Connections

Toolbox

counters

Key Words

dividend

divisor

quotient

You can use division to divide a total number of objects into equal groups.

Taya has 24 shells. She wants to divide them into equal groups. She can write division sentences to describe ways to divide 24 shells into equal groups.

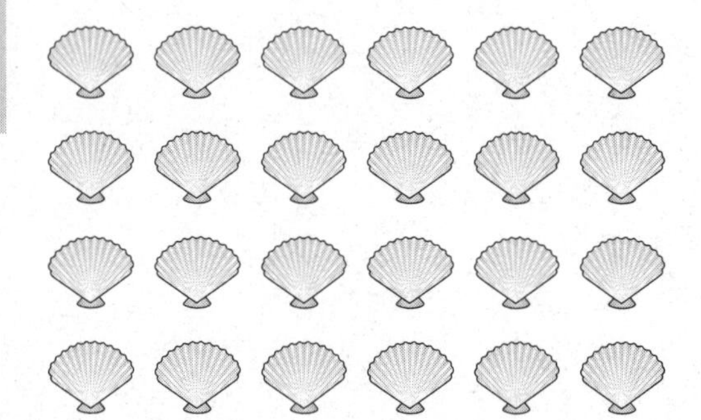

There are 24 shells.

There are 4 rows of shells.

There are 6 shells in each row.

$24 \div 4 = 6$ or $24 \div 6 = 4$

There are two ways to write division sentences with symbols.

The **dividend** is the number that is divided. The **divisor** is the number that divides the dividend. The **quotient** is the answer in a division problem.

divisor → $4\overline{)8}$ ← dividend, with 2 ← quotient above

dividend → $8 \div 4 = 2$ ← quotient

division ↑ divisor

Take It Apart

Follow these steps to write division sentences.

Step 1 Find the total number of objects, or the dividend.

Step 2 Decide how many groups the dividend is divided into or how many objects are in each group. This is the divisor.

Step 3 Use the dividend and the divisor to write a division sentence.

Step 4 Find the quotient.

There are 14 hearts.

There are 7 groups.

There are 2 hearts in each group.

$14 \div 7 = 2$ or $14 \div 2 = 7$

Write a division sentence to describe the total number of objects divided into equal groups.

1. 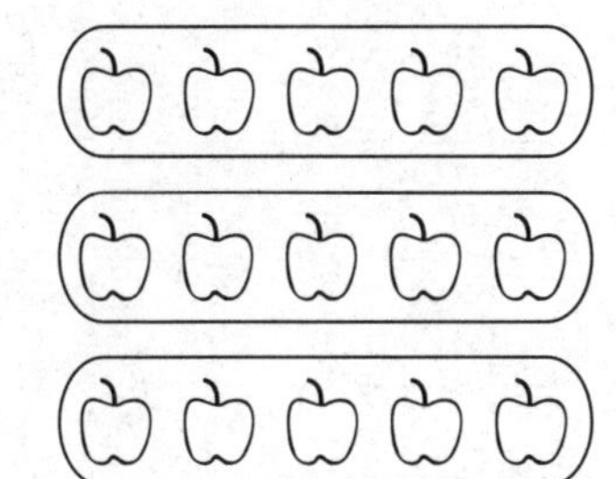

_____ ÷ _____ = _____

or _____ ÷ _____ = _____

2. 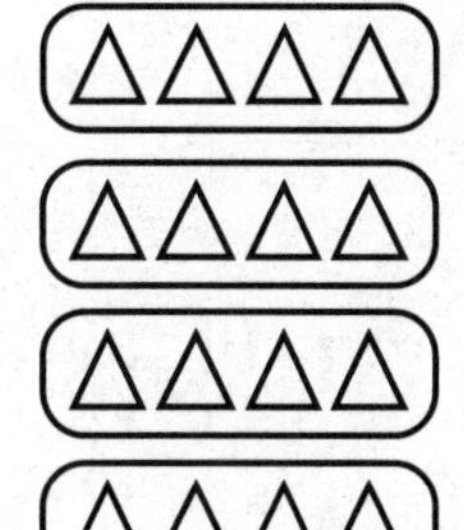

_____ ÷ _____ = _____

Put It Together

Use what you know about equal groups and division to write division sentences. Find the quotient.

1.

_____ ÷ _____ = _____

or

_____ ÷ _____ = _____

2.

_____ ÷ _____ = _____

or

_____ ÷ _____ = _____

3.

_____ ÷ _____ = _____

4.

_____ ÷ _____ = _____

or

_____ ÷ _____ = _____

Answer the questions. Share your ideas with a classmate.

5. If the dividend is the total number of objects and the divisor is the number of objects in one group, what is the quotient?

____

6. Tony has 18 pineapples. He wants to divide them into equal groups. Describe a situation in which he could write the number of pineapples in each group as 18 ÷ 6.

____

____

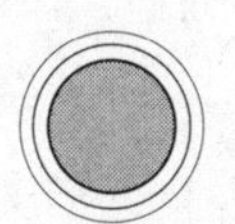

Make It Work

Answer the questions below.

1. Which expression tells how many dog treats are in each row?

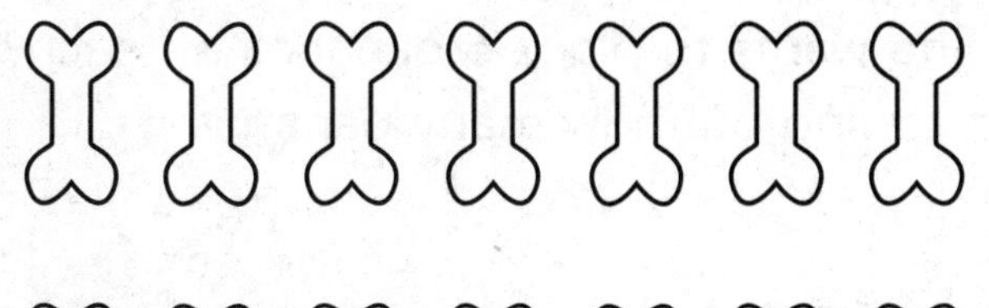

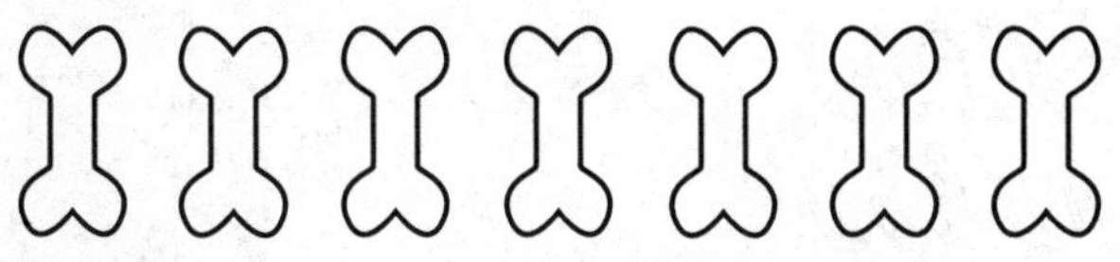

A. $7 + 7$ **B.** $14 \div 2$

C. 2×7 **D.** $2 + 14$

2. Which expression describes the number of stickers in each group?

There are 21 stickers. The stickers are divided into 3 equal groups.

A. $21 \div 3 = 7$ **B.** $21 + 3 = 24$

C. $21 - 3 = 18$ **D.** $21 \times 3 = 63$

3. Raul has 36 toy cars. He lines them up in rows of 9. Write a division expression to describe how many toy cars are in each row.

____

4. Connor has 18 cups of cereal. He eats 2 cups every morning. How many days can he eat cereal before he runs out?

____

5. Write a situation that could be described by the division expression $15 \div 3$. What is the quotient?

____

____

Lesson 3 Using Multiplication to Solve Word Problems

3.OA.3 Use multiplication and division within 100 to solve word problems in situations involving equal groups, arrays, and measurement quantities, e.g., by using drawings and equations with a symbol for the unknown number to represent the problem.

Real World Connections

Toolbox
counters

Key Word
variable

You can use multiplication to solve word problems with equal groups.

A grocer is placing bananas in the produce section of a grocery store. She has 7 shelves for bananas. She wants to place 6 bananas on each shelf. She can use multiplication to find out how many bananas she needs.

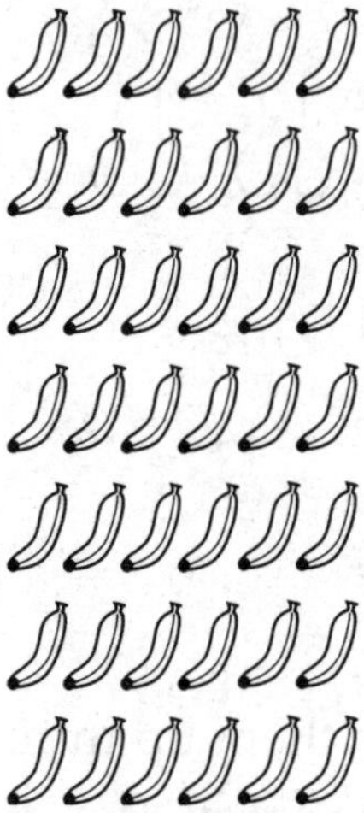

You can use an array like the one of the bananas to help you solve the problem. You can also write a multiplication equation using a variable to solve the problem. A **variable** is a symbol, like a letter, that represents an unknown number.

7	$\times$	6	$=$	b
shelves		bananas on each shelf		total number of bananas

Multiply 7×6 to find b.

$7 \times 6 = 42$

So $b = 42$.

Take It Apart

Follow these steps to solve a word problem using multiplication.

Step 1 Read the problem carefully to find the information you are given.

Step 2 Decide what you need to find out.

Step 3 Write a multiplication sentence with a variable for the unknown number.

Step 4 Multiply to solve. Does your answer make sense?

Angela ordered 6 pizzas for a picnic. Each pizza has 8 slices. How many slices are there altogether?

What information are you given?

- how many pizzas were ordered
- how many slices each pizza has

These are the factors.

What do you need to find out?

- how many slices of pizza there are altogether

This is the multiplication sentence.
$6 \times 8 = s$

$6 \times 8 = 48$, so there are 48 slices of pizza in all.

Solve each problem. Use counters if you need help.

1. Julian has an album for his trading cards. Each page holds 5 cards. How many cards are on 9 pages?

   ____

2. Alexis has 3 baskets of oranges. Each basket has 8 oranges in it. How many oranges are in the baskets?

   ____

Put It Together

Use what you know about solving word problems and multiplication to solve these problems. Use counters if you need help.

1. Maya bought 4 boxes of pencils. There are 8 pencils in each box. How many pencils did she buy in all?

______

2. An aquarium has 3 tanks with angelfish in them. If there are 12 angelfish in each tank, how many angelfish are at the aquarium?

______

3. Tristan has 2 cartons of eggs. There are 18 eggs in each carton. If he uses all of the eggs today making breakfast and baking, how many eggs will he use?

______

4. Josie earns $5 for each day she takes care of her neighbor's dog. How much will she earn if she takes care of the dog for 9 days?

______

5. A store sold 15 books yesterday. Each book cost $6. How much money did the store make selling the books?

______

6. For an art project, each student needs 8 pieces of paper. How many pieces of paper does the teacher need to have if there are 9 students in the class?

______

Answer the questions. Share your ideas with a classmate.

7. How do you know when to use multiplication to solve a word problem?

______

______

8. Meredith has 3 necklaces that each have 8 beads. Clara has 4 necklaces that each have 6 beads. Who has more beads on her necklaces? Explain.

______

______

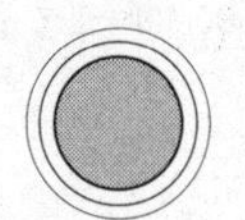

Make It Work

Answer the questions below.

1. Dylan has four ten-dollar bills. How much money does Dylan have?

A. $4

B. $10

C. $20

D. $40

2. The chairs in Ms. Gina's music class are arranged in 4 rows of 8 chairs. How many chairs are there in all?

A. 12 chairs

B. 32 chairs

C. 36 chairs

D. 40 chairs

3. Erin buys 5 packages of hot dog buns for a picnic. Each package has 8 buns. How many hot dogs did she buy if she wants to use all the buns?

____

4. Sadie places 1 slice of bread on each of 8 plates. Write a multiplication sentence to show how many slices of bread Sadie places on the plates in all.

____

5. Tad wants to buy 4 movie tickets. Each ticket costs $7. He has 2 ten-dollar bills. Does he have enough money to buy the tickets? Explain.

____

____

Lesson 4 Using Division to Solve Word Problems

3.OA.3 Use multiplication and division within 100 to solve word problems in situations involving equal groups, arrays, and measurement quantities, e.g., by using drawings and equations with a symbol for the unknown number to represent the problem.

Real World Connections

Toolbox

counters

Key Words

dividend
divisor
quotient
variable

You can use division to solve word problems in which objects are separated into groups.

Kacia has 25 balloons. She separates them into groups of 5. She can use division to find out how many balloons will be in each group.

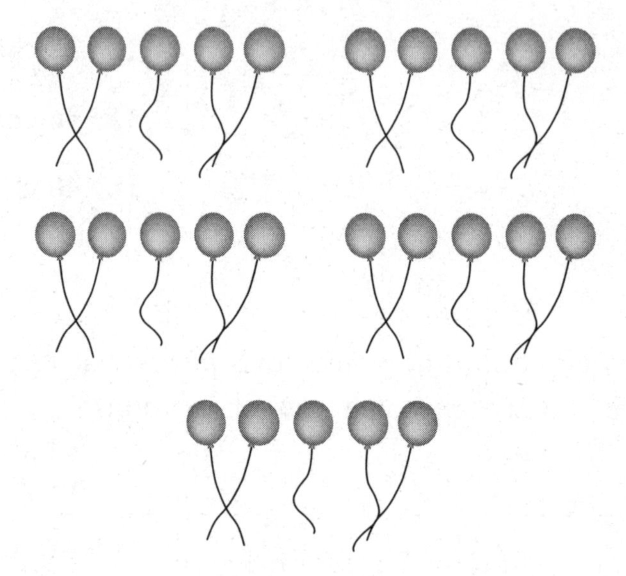

The total number of objects to be divided is the **dividend**.
The number in each group or the number of groups is the **divisor**.
The **quotient** is the answer. In this problem, the quotient is the number of balloons in each group. Use a **variable** to represent the unknown number.

Divide the dividend by the divisor to find the quotient.

25	÷	5	=	g
balloons		number of groups		balloons in each group
25	÷	5	=	5

$25 \div 5 = 5$

$g = 5$

Take It Apart

Follow these steps to solve a word problem using division.

Step 1 Read the problem carefully. What information are you given?

Step 2 Decide what you need to find out.

Step 3 Write a division sentence with a variable for the unknown number.

Step 4 Divide to solve. Does your answer make sense?

Eric has 15 coins. He separates them into 3 equal groups.
How many coins are in each group?

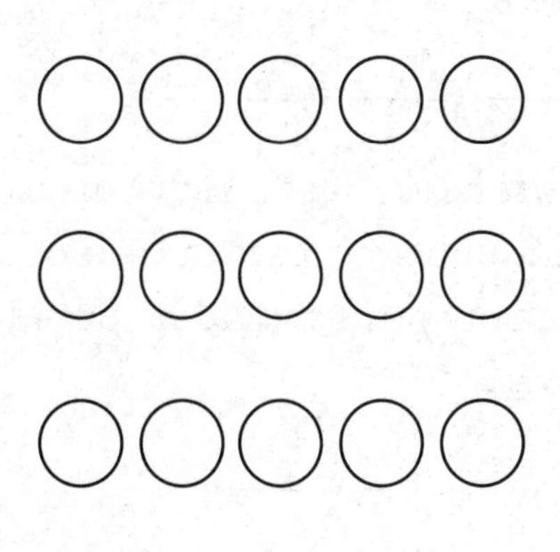

What information are you given?

- how many coins Eric has
- how many groups he separates the coins into

These are the dividend and the divisor.

What do you need to find out?

- how many coins are in each group

This is the quotient.

$15 \div 3 = c$

$15 \div 3 = 5$, so there are 5 coins in each group.

Solve each problem. Use counters if you need help.

1. Carlie wants to give each of her 4 friends the same number of stickers. She has 20 stickers. How many stickers will each friend get?

   ____

2. Elliot has 42 crayons. He gives 6 crayons to each child. How many children did he give crayons to?

   ____

Put It Together

Use division to solve these problems. Use counters if you need to help.

1. Victoria buys notebooks that cost $2 each. How many notebooks can she buy with $12?

____

2. Antonio bought sandwiches for his family for lunch. He spent $30. If he spent $6 on each sandwich, how many sandwiches did he buy?

____

3. A farmer has 64 tomato plants. He plants 8 tomato plants in each row. How many rows does he plant?

____

4. Martha and her 5 friends share 45 grapes equally. How many grapes does each person get?

____

5. Maren needs 3 googly eyes for each puppet she is making. If she has 27 googly eyes, how many puppets can she make?

____

6. A florist has 72 roses. He wants to put an equal number of roses in each of 8 vases. How many roses should he put in each vase?

____

Answer the questions. Share your ideas with a classmate.

7. There are 49 kids at a summer camp. A counselor wants to separate them into equal groups. How many equal groups can the counselor make? Explain.

____

____

8. Grace has 36 beads separated into groups of 4. Keesha has 54 beads separated into groups of 9. Does Grace or Keesha have more beads in each group? Explain.

____

____

____

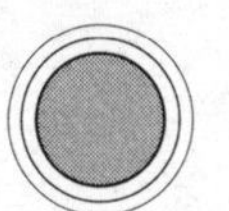

Make It Work

Answer the questions below.

1. Carter has $64. He buys 8 of the same t-shirt. What is the cost of one t-shirt?

A. $4

B. $8

C. $56

D. $72

2. Elizabeth and her 3 friends share 24 markers equally. How many markers does each person get?

A. 4 markers

B. 5 markers

C. 6 markers

D. 8 markers

3. Chao wants to buy 5 movies that each cost $6. He has $24. Can he buy the 5 movies?

____

4. Alisha has 42 rubber balls. She separates them into equal groups. What could be the number of groups she separates them into? How many balls will be in each group?

____

5. Taylor has 3 pizzas. She has invited 5 people to eat the pizzas with her. If she plans on each person eating 4 slices of pizza, into how many slices should Taylor cut each pizza? Explain.

____

____

Determine the Unknown in an Equation

3.OA.4 Determine the unknown whole number in a multiplication or division equation relating three whole numbers. *For example, determine the unknown number that makes the equation true in each of the equations* $8 \times ? = 48$, $5 = \square \div 3$, $6 \times 6 = ?$.

Real World Connections

Key Words

unknown

variable

You have 21 puppies. The same number of puppies were born to each of 3 mother dogs. How many puppies does each mother dog have? You can solve problems like this by finding the **unknown**, or missing number, in an equation.

$3 \times \boxed{7} = 21$

You can use a $\square$, a ?, or a letter to stand for the missing number. A letter that stands for a missing number in an equation is called a **variable**.

An unknown in a multiplication equation can be a factor or the product.

3	×	$\boxed{7}$	=	21
factor		factor		product

An unknown in a division equation can be the dividend, the divisor, or the quotient.

21	÷	$\boxed{7}$	=	3
dividend		divisor		quotient

So $3 \times 7 = 21$ and $21 \div 7 = 3$.

Take It Apart

Follow these steps to find an unknown in a multiplication or division equation.

Step 1 Look at the equation. Find the symbol that stands for the unknown.

$\boxed{30} \div 5 = 6$

The box stands for the unknown. The unknown is the dividend in the equation.

Step 2 Think about how the numbers are related.

Think: *What number divided by 5 equals 6?*

Step 3 Use the multiplication and division facts you know to help you.

Think of multiplication and division facts that include both 5 and 6.

You know $5 \times 6 = 30$.

Step 4 Choose a number to try in the equation to see if it makes the equation true.

Try 30.

$30 \div 5 = 6$. The equation is true.

30 is the unknown in $\boxed{30} \div 5 = 6$.

Find the unknown that makes each equation true.

1. $40 \div 5 = a$

   8

2. $4 \times \boxed{3} = 12$

   3

3. $6 = \boxed{18} \div 3$

   18

4. $\boxed{7} \times 7 = 49$

   7

Put It Together

Find the unknown that makes each equation true.

1. $4 \times ? = 24$

6

2. $35 \div b = 7$

5

3. $? \times 8 = 72$

9

4. $42 \div 6 = \boxed{7}$

7

5. $5 \times 5 = \boxed{25}$

25

6. $21 = 3 \times ?$

7

7. $16 = \boxed{8} \times 2$

8

8. $? = 48 \div 8$

6

9. $5 \times 4 = t$

20

10. $36 \div x = 9$

4

11. $54 = 9 \times ?$

6

12. $8 \times \boxed{7} = 56$

7

Answer the questions. Share your ideas with a classmate.

13. Six people are playing a game. One player hands out 36 cards. Each player has the same number of cards. How many cards does each player have? Explain.

Each player has 6 cards becuse 6 x 36 = 6.

14. What number makes this equation true? Explain how you found the number.

$6 \times \boxed{4} = 8 \times 3$

It true becus 3 x 8 = 24.

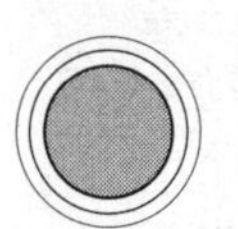

Make It Work

Answer the questions below.

1. What number makes the equation true?

$5 \times 9 = ?$

A. 27

B. 36

C. 40

D. 45

2. Aliyah has 24 flashcards. They are in 3 equal groups on her desk. How many flashcards are in each group?

$24 = 3 \times \square$ 8

A. 4 flashcards

B. 6 flashcards

C. 8 flashcards

D. 9 flashcards

3. Ekani did 6 sets of jumping jacks. She did 48 jumping jacks in all. How many jumping jacks did she do in each set?

$6 \times \square = 48$ (8)

She did 8 jumping jacks each set.

4. Jasper packed 35 pineapples equally into 7 boxes. How many pineapples are in each box?

They were 5 in each box.

5. Ms. Granger wrote this equation on the board. She forgot the operation symbol. What symbol makes the equation true? Explain how you decided.

$72 = 8 \square 9$ (×)

I picked this symbol becuse I tried doing 9÷8 but it dose not give you 72. So I did 9x8 witch gives me 72.

Applying Properties of Operations

3.OA.5 Apply properties of operations as strategies to multiply and divide. *Examples: If $6 \times 4 = 24$ is known, then $4 \times 6 = 24$ is also known. (Commutative property of multiplication.) $3 \times 5 \times 2$ can be found by $3 \times 5 = 15$, then $15 \times 2 = 30$, or by $5 \times 2 = 10$, then $3 \times 10 = 30$. (Associative property of multiplication.) Knowing that $8 \times 5 = 40$ and $8 \times 2 = 16$, one can find 8×7 as $8 \times (5 + 2) = (8 \times 5) + (8 \times 2) = 40 + 16 = 56$. (Distributive property.)*

Real World Connections

Key Words

Commutative property of multiplication

Associative property of multiplication

Distributive property of multiplication

For a game, your teacher separates you and your classmates into 6 teams. Each team has 4 students. How many students are there in all? You would multiply 6×4 to find out.

You can use properties of multiplication to make multiplying easier. You may use more than one property to find a product.

Properties of Multiplication	
Commutative property of multiplication You can multiply two factors in any order. The product is the same. $6 \times 4 = 24$ $4 \times 6 = 24$ $6 \times 4 = 4 \times 6$	**Associative property of multiplication** You can group factors in different ways. The product is the same. $(2 \times 4) \times 3 = 2 \times (4 \times 3)$ $8 \times 3 = 2 \times 12$ $24 = 24$

Distributive property of multiplication

You can break apart factors to get facts that you know.

```
* * * * * *
* * * * * *
-----------
* * * * * *
* * * * * *
* * * * * *
```

$5 \times 6 = ?$

Think: $5 = 2 + 3$, so
5 groups of 6 = 2 groups of 6 + 3 groups of 6

$5 \times 6 = (2 + 3) \times 6$

$= (2 \times 6) + (3 \times 6)$

$= 12 + 18$

$= 30$

Take It Apart

Follow these steps to find a product using the properties of multiplication.

Step 1 Look at the multiplication sentence. Would it be helpful to change the order of the factors, change how they are grouped, or break apart one of the factors?

Step 2 Choose a multiplication property to help you.

Step 3 Multiply.

$(3 \times 5) \times 2 =$ ______

You can group factors in different ways. Group them so they are easy to multiply.

$$(3 \times 5) \times 2 = 3 \times (5 \times 2)$$
$$= 3 \times 10$$
$$= 30$$

Find each product.

1. $5 \times 8 = 40$

   $8 \times 5 =$ ______

2. $3 \times 6 = 18$

   $6 \times 3 =$ ______

3. $4 \times 9 = 36$

   $9 \times 4 =$ ______

4. $(2 \times 4) \times 3 = 24$

   $2 \times (4 \times 3) =$ ______

5. $(4 \times 6) \times 2 = 48$

   $4 \times (6 \times 2) =$ ______

6. $3 \times (2 \times 7) = 42$

   $(3 \times 2) \times 7 =$ ______

7. $9 \times 4 = 36$

   $(3 \times 4) + (6 \times 4) =$ ______

8. $8 \times 4 = 32$

   $(3 \times 4) + (5 \times 4) =$ ______

Put It Together

Find the product.

1. $3 \times 7 =$ _____

   $7 \times 3 =$ _____

2. $(3 \times 5) \times 2 =$ _____

   $3 \times (5 \times 2) =$ _____

3. $6 \times 3 =$ _____

   $3 \times 6 =$ _____

4. $(6 \times 5) \times 2 =$ _____

   $6 \times (5 \times 2) =$ _____

5. $(4 \times 3) \times 1 =$ _____

   $4 \times (3 \times 1) =$ _____

6. $9 \times 5 =$ _____

   $5 \times 9 =$ _____

7. $7 \times 5 =$ _____

   $(3 \times 5) + (4 \times 5) =$ _____

8. $9 \times 3 =$ _____

   $(7 \times 3) + (2 \times 3) =$ _____

9. $8 \times 5 =$ _____

   $(5 \times 5) + (3 \times 5) =$ _____

10. $7 \times 3 =$ _____

    $(6 \times 3) + (1 \times 3) =$ _____

Answer the questions. Share your ideas with a classmate.

11. Cora and Aidan both multiply $4 \times 3 \times 2$. Cora multiplies 4×3 first and then the 2. Aidan multiplies 2×3 first and then the 4. Who will get the correct answer? Explain your thinking.

    ____

    ____

12. Ms. Potts has 24 desks in her classroom. They are placed in 4 rows of 6. Can she place them in 6 equal rows? Explain.

    ____

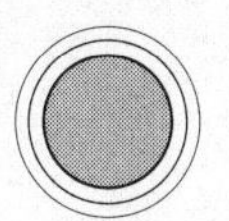

Make It Work

Answer the questions below.

1. What expression has the same product as $(4 \times 6) \times 1$?

A. $4 \times (6 \times 3)$
B. $4 \times (6 \times 1)$
C. $4 \times (1 \times 7)$
D. $4 \times (2 \times 4)$

2. Maria has 3 apples in each of 7 baskets. She wants to use only 3 baskets for the apples. How many apples must she put in each basket?

A. 3 apples
B. 5 apples
C. 6 apples
D. 7 apples

3. Tomas puts his books in 7 groups of 5. What is another way he can group his books?

____

4. What is the missing number? Explain.

$3 \times (8 \times 2) = (3 \times 8) \times$ ________

____

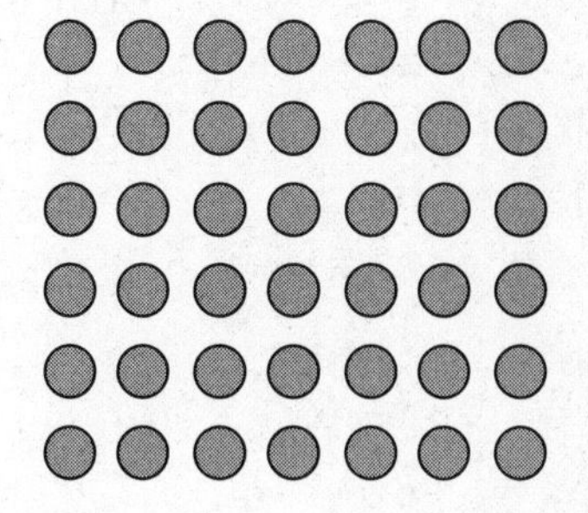

5. Look at the array. How can you use the array to find 6×7? Draw a line to break the array into 2 parts. Then write the number sentences to show how to find the product. Write the product. Explain what you did.

____

____

____

____

Lesson 7 Relating Division to Multiplication

3.OA.6 Understand division as an unknown-factor problem. *For example, find 32 ÷ 8 by finding the number that makes 32 when multiplied by 8.*

Real World Connections

Key Word

fact family

How do you share a bunch of grapes with a friend so you each get the same amount? You use division.

You can use multiplication to help you divide because multiplication and division are related. They are opposite operations. One operation undoes the other.

A group of related multiplication and division facts that use the same numbers is a **fact family**.

Fact Family for 3, 4, 12	
$3 \times 4 = 12$	$12 \div 4 = 3$
$4 \times 3 = 12$	$12 \div 3 = 4$

You can use fact families to help you solve division problems. Rewrite the division problem as a multiplication problem. Then find the missing factor.

$12 \div 3 =$ ______

______ $\times 3 = 12$

$4 \times 3 = 12$, so $12 \div 3 = 4$

Take It Apart

Follow these steps to use multiplication to help you solve a division problem.

Step 1 Look at the division problem. Rewrite the division problem as a multiplication problem with a missing factor.

$$24 \div 4 = \_\_\_\_$$

$$\_\_\_\_ \times 4 = 24$$

Step 2 Find the missing factor. Use fact families to help you.

Think: What number multiplied by 4 equals 24?

$$\_\_\_\_ \times 4 = 24$$

$$6 \times 4 = 24$$

So $24 \div 4 = 6$.

Find the missing number. Use the related multiplication fact to help you.

1. $16 \div 2 = \_\_\_\_$

   $8 \times 2 = 16$

2. $25 \div 5 = \_\_\_\_$

   $5 \times 5 = 25$

3. $54 \div 9 = \_\_\_\_$

   $6 \times 9 = 54$

4. $21 \div 3 = \_\_\_\_$

   $7 \times 3 = 21$

5. $28 \div 7 = \_\_\_\_$

   $4 \times 7 = 28$

6. $48 \div 6 = \_\_\_\_$

   $8 \times 6 = 48$

Put It Together

Solve each division problem. Write the related multiplication fact to help you.

1. $12 \div 6 =$ ______

______ $\times 6 = 12$

2. $24 \div 3 =$ ______

______ $\times 3 = 24$

3. $72 \div 8 =$ ______

______ $\times 8 = 72$

4. $49 \div 7 =$ ______

______ $\times 7 = 49$

5. $15 \div 3 =$ ______

______ $\times 3 = 15$

6. $56 \div 8 =$ ______

______ $\times 8 = 56$

7. $32 \div 4 =$ ______

______ $\times 4 = 32$

8. $63 \div 7 =$ ______

______ $\times 7 = 63$

9. $16 \div 4 =$ ______

______ $\times 4 = 16$

10. $42 \div 7 =$ ______

______ $\times 7 = 42$

11. $40 \div 8 =$ ______

______ $\times 8 = 40$

12. $45 \div 5 =$ ______

______ $\times 5 = 45$

Answer the questions. Share your ideas with a classmate.

13. Miranda writes the problem $28 \div 4 = 7$. Write a multiplication sentence she can use to check her answer.

____

14. Caden has 24 sheets of paper. He puts an equal number of sheets of paper on each of 6 desks. How many sheets of paper are on each desk? Explain how you can use a multiplication fact to help you.

____

____

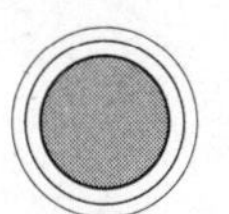

Make It Work

Answer the questions below.

1. Freddy thinks that $32 \div 4 = 8$. Which multiplication fact could he use to check his answer?

A. $8 - 4 = 4$

B. $4 + 8 = 12$

C. $32 - 4 = 28$

D. $4 \times 8 = 32$

2. Candace has 18 pancakes to divide evenly among 3 people. How many pancakes will each person get? Use a multiplication fact to help you.

A. 3 pancakes

B. 6 pancakes

C. 15 pancakes

D. 21 pancakes

3. A group of 30 students is going on a field trip. Each van they are using can take 6 students. How many vans will they need to go on the field trip?

____

4. Helena separates 42 kids into 7 teams at summer camp. How many kids are on each team? Write the multiplication fact you use to help you divide.

____

5. William used the multiplication fact $3 \times 8 = 24$ to help him divide $24 \div 6$. He decides $24 \div 6 = 8$. What is his error? Find the correct answer and explain what William did incorrectly.

____

____

____

Multiplying and Dividing Within 100

3.OA.7 Fluently multiply and divide within 100, using strategies such as the relationship between multiplication and division (e.g., knowing that $8 \times 5 = 40$, one knows that $40 \div 5 = 8$) or properties of operations. By the end of Grade 3, know from memory all products of two one-digit numbers.

Real World Connections

Key Word

fact families

You use multiplication and division everyday to solve all kinds of problems. If your teacher gives you 48 pencils to place on 6 tables, how many pencils should you put on each table? Division can tell you!

There are many strategies to help you multiply and divide. Remember, multiplication and division are related. One undoes the other. Understanding **fact families** can help. If you know one fact, you know four facts.

Fact Family for 3, 8, 24	
$3 \times 8 = 24$	$24 \div 8 = 3$
$8 \times 3 = 24$	$24 \div 3 = 8$

You can also use properties of multiplication to help you multiply and divide.

You can multiply factors in any order. The product is the same.

$a \times b = b \times a$ $\quad$ $2 \times 4 = 4 \times 2$

You can group factors in different ways. The product is the same.

$(a \times b) \times c = a \times (b \times c)$ $\quad$ $(2 \times 4) \times 3 = 2 \times (4 \times 3)$

You can break apart factors to help you multiply.

$5 \times 7 = 5 \times (5 + 2) = (5 \times 5) + (5 \times 2) = 25 + 10 = 35$

When you multiply a number by 0, the product is 0.

$0 \times 2 = 0$

When you multiply a number by 1, the product is the number.

$4 \times 1 = 4$

Take It Apart

Follow these hints to multiply and divide within 100.

Step 1 Look at the problem and the numbers in the problem carefully. How are they related?

Step 2 Think about the different strategies you know to help you multiply and divide. Will one of the strategies help you?

Step 3 Multiply or divide. You may use none, one, or more than one strategy to help you.

Examples:

$8 \times 5 =$ _____	$72 \div 9 =$ _____	$9 \times 5 =$ _____
Think about facts you know. $5 \times 8 = 40$ So $8 \times 5 = 40$	Think: What number multiplied by 9 equals 72? $8 \times 9 = 72$ So $72 \div 9 = 8$	Break apart the 9. $= (4 + 5) \times 5$ $= (4 \times 5) + (5 \times 5)$ $= 20 + 25$ $= 45$

Multiply or divide. Use the different strategies to help you.

1. $42 \div 7 =$ _____

   $6 \times 7 = 42$

2. $24 \div 6 =$ _____

   $24 \div 4 = 6$

3. $0 \times 6 =$ _____

   $0 \times 1 = 0$

4. $8 \times 7 =$ _____

   $(8 \times 5) + (8 \times 2) = 40 + 16 = 56$

5. $9 \times 6 =$ _____

   $(9 \times 5) + (9 \times 1) = 45 + 9 = 54$

Put It Together

Multiply or Divide.

1. $6 \times 3 =$ ______ **2.** $9 \times 2 =$ ______ **3.** $7 \times 9 =$ ______

4. $5 \times 4 =$ ______ **5.** $7 \times 3 =$ ______ **6.** $3 \times 9 =$ ______

7. $\begin{array}{r} 8 \\ \times\ 4 \\ \hline \end{array}$ **8.** $\begin{array}{r} 9 \\ \times\ 5 \\ \hline \end{array}$ **9.** $\begin{array}{r} 6 \\ \times\ 6 \\ \hline \end{array}$ **10.** $\begin{array}{r} 4 \\ \times\ 8 \\ \hline \end{array}$ **11.** $\begin{array}{r} 6 \\ \times\ 5 \\ \hline \end{array}$

12. $4\overline{)32}$ **13.** $7\overline{)63}$ **14.** $2\overline{)14}$

15. $3\overline{)24}$ **16.** $4\overline{)16}$ **17.** $36 \div 9 =$ ______

18. $18 \div 3 =$ ______ **19.** $12 \div 2 =$ ______ **20.** $81 \div 9 =$ ______

21. $42 \div 6 =$ ______ **22.** $40 \div 5 =$ ______

Answer the questions. Share your ideas with a classmate.

23. Julian has 48 crayons. There are 6 crayons in each box. How many boxes does he have? Explain how you found your answer.

____

____

24. Mae has 9 bags of stones. She has 7 stones in each bag. Show how to break apart the factor 7 to find out how many stones she has in all.

____

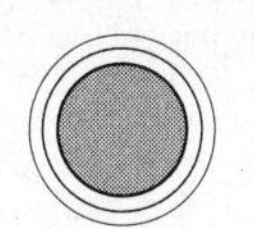

Make It Work

Answer the questions below.

1. Ms. Lofgren has 5 tables in her classroom. Six students sit at each table. How many students are in Ms. Lofgren's class?

A. 25

B. 30

C. 35

D. 40

2. A pet store has 42 new hamsters. How many cages will they need for the hamsters if they put 7 hamsters in each cage?

A. 4

B. 5

C. 6

D. 7

3. Jalisa has 3 baskets. There are 0 pears in each basket. Write a multiplication sentence to show how many pears there are in all.

____

4. Mr. Markham has 40 chairs to place in rows for a class program. If he places them in 5 rows, how many chairs will be in each row? Explain the strategy you used to find your answer.

____

5. Bryce makes 24 muffins. He wants to share the muffins equally with his 3 friends. How many muffins will each person get? Explain how you solved the problem.

____

____

____

Lesson 9 Solving Two-Step Word Problems

3.OA.8 Solve two-step word problems using the four operations. Represent these problems using equations with a letter standing for the unknown quantity. Assess the reasonableness of answers using mental computation and estimation strategies including rounding.

Real World Connections

Key Word

order of operations

Imagine you have 4 packages of hot dog buns at a picnic. Each package has 8 buns. At the end of the picnic, there are 10 buns left. How can you find out how many buns got eaten?

Sometimes it takes more than one step to solve a problem. It might also take more than one operation to solve a problem. Use key words to help you decide if you need to add, subtract, multiply, or divide to solve a problem.

Addition	Subtraction	Multiplication	Division
add	difference	times	each
altogether	fewer	every	out of
both	how many more	of	quotient
in all	how much more	increased by	even groups
total	how much left	multiplied by	
combined	decreased by	product of	
sum			

Remember to follow the **order of operations** with each step of the problem.

Order of Operations

1) Do any operations in parentheses.

2) Work from left to right, multiplying and dividing.

3) Work from left to right, adding and subtracting.

Take It Apart

To solve multi-step problems, follow these steps.

Step 1 Read the problem carefully. What information is given? What are you asked to find?

Sadie bought 8 notebooks. Each notebook cost $2. She paid with a twenty-dollar bill. What is her change?

What information is given? Sadie bought 8 notebooks. Each notebook cost $2. She paid with a twenty-dollar bill.

What are you asked to find? How much change she gets.

Step 2 Make a plan. Break the problem into smaller parts and decide how to solve each part.

What operation should you use to find how much the notebooks cost in all? multiplication

What operation should you use to find how much change she gets? subtraction

Step 3 Solve the problem.

$8 \times \$2 = \$16$ $\quad\quad$ $\$20 - \$16 = \$4$

Step 4 Check your answer. Work backward from your answer.

$\$20 - \$4 = \$16$ $\quad\quad$ $\$16 \div 2 = 8$, so the answer is correct.

Solve each problem.

1. Alayna bought 3 pizzas. Each pizza has 8 slices. She and her five friends ate 14 slices of pizza altogether. How many slices are left?

   $3 \times 8 =$ 24 $\quad\quad$ 24 $- 14 =$ 10 slices left

2. Karsten has 16 blue marbles, and 14 red marbles. He wants to divide his marbles into groups of 5. How many marbles will be in each group?

   $16 + 14 =$ 30 $\quad\quad$ 30 $\div 5 =$ 6 marbles

Put It Together

Solve each problem.

1. Tickets to a play are $5 for children and $8 for adults. How much will tickets to the play cost for 3 children and 2 adults?

   31 $8 \times 2 = 16$ $5 \times 3 = 15$ 16 + 15 = 31

2. Elizabeth bought baskets for her shelves. She bought 3 sets of baskets. Each set has 8 baskets. She will divide the baskets evenly between 4 shelves. How many baskets will be on each shelf?

   6 $8 \times 3 = 24 \div 4 = 6$

3. Kirk wants to ride his bike 30 miles in the next 5 days. He misses the first two days because it rains. If he rides the same number of miles each of the remaining days, how many miles does he ride each day?

   10 $30 \div 6 = 10$

4. Mi-Cha and four friends each have 9 crackers. They each eat 2 crackers. Now how many crackers do they have in all?

   35 $5 \times 9 = 45$ $5 \times 2 = 10$

Answer the questions. Share your ideas with a classmate.

5. Luisa has 8 bags of apples with 72 apples. Each bag has the same number of apples. She adds 8 apples to the last bag of apples. How many apples are in the last bag now? Explain how you found your answer.

   They are 17 apples in the last bag becuse 72 ÷ 8 = 9

6. Josie sold 8 tomato plants from her garden store. She still has 6 tomato plants each in 7 containers. How many tomato plants did she start with? Explain how you found your answer.

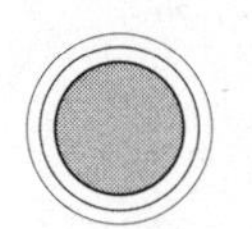

Make It Work

Answer the questions below.

1. Javier practiced 6 pages of spelling words. Julia practiced 5 pages of spelling words. There are 8 spelling words on each page. How many spelling words did they practice in all?

   A. 30 B. 40

   C. 48 D. 88

2. Lia read 12 pages of a book each afternoon for 4 days. The book has 64 pages. How many pages does she have left to read to finish the book?

   A. 12 B. 48

   C. 16 D. 18

   12x4=46 64 − 46 = 18

3. Maggie has 5 packages of beads. Each package has 8 beads. If she uses 10 beads for each necklace she makes, how many necklaces can she make with her beads? Show your work.

   She can make 30 necklaces with her beads.
   5x8=40-10=30

4. Sebastian had $20. He spent $6 on lunch. He wants to buy 3 games that each cost $5. Does he have enough money to buy the games? Explain.

   Yes, becuse 20-6=14 and 3x5=15 and then 15-14=10.

   20-6=14 3x5=15 15 − 14 = 01

5. Natalia made 4 batches of granola. Each batch has 6 cups of granola. She already had 3 cups of granola. She wants to divide all of the granola equally into 3 bags. She adds 6 + 3 and then multiplies by 4 to get 36 cups of granola. Then she divides by 3 to find that she needs 12 bags. How many bags does she actually need? Explain what she did incorrectly.

   6x4=24 +3 = 27

   Natalia actually needs 3 bags, you can divied 27 in 3 bags.

   7÷3=21

Lesson 10 Identifying Arithmetic Patterns

3.OA.9 Identify arithmetic patterns (including patterns in the addition table or multiplication table), and explain them using properties of operations. *For example, observe that 4 times a number is always even, and explain why 4 times a number can be decomposed into two equal addends.*

Real World Connections

Key Word

arithmetic pattern

There are patterns all around you. Some patterns use shapes. Others use numbers. A pattern that uses numbers is called an **arithmetic pattern**.

All patterns have rules. A rule tells you what to do to one number to get the next number.

Rule: Multiply by 6	
Number of Insects	**Number of Legs**
1	6
2	12
3	18
4	24
5	30

The rule for the pattern in the table on the left is multiply by 6. When you multiply the number in the left column by 6, you get the number in the right column. Another way to describe the pattern is multiply by 2, then multiply by 3, because 2 and 3 are factors of 6. Since 6 is an even number, the product of any number multiplied by 6 will also be even.

Patterns in the Multiplication Table

You can also find arithmetic patterns in tables like the multiplication table. For example, to complete the facts with 2 as a factor, you can skip count by 2s, or use the rule add 2.

	1	**2**	**3**	**4**	**5**	**6**	**7**	**8**	**9**	**10**
1	1	2	3	4	5	6	7	8	9	10
2	2	4	6	8	10	12	14	16	18	20
3	3	6	9	12	15	18	21	24	27	30
4	4	8	12	16	20	24	28	32	36	40
5	5	10	15	20	25	30	35	40	45	50
6	6	12	18	24	30	36	42	48	54	60
7	7	14	21	28	35	42	49	56	63	70
8	8	16	24	32	40	48	56	64	72	80
9	9	18	27	36	45	54	63	72	81	90
10	10	20	30	40	50	60	70	80	90	100

Take It Apart

To identify patterns in numbers, follow these steps.

Step 1 Look at the numbers closely.

Decide which operation to try.

You add or multiply to get a greater number.

You subtract or divide to get a smaller number.

Lemonade Recipe

Cups of Mix	Cups of Water
1	3
2	6
3	9

Step 2 Try a rule for the first pair of numbers.

$1 + \_\_\_\_ = 3$ Add 2.

$1 \times \_\_\_\_ = 3$ Multiply by 3.

Step 3 Try the second pair of numbers to see which rule works.

$2 + 2 = 6$ This is not true. Add 2 does not work.

$2 \times 3 = 6$ This is true. Multiply by 3 works.

Write each rule another way.

1.

Number of Songs	Time to Practice
2	16
4	32
6	48

Multiply by 8.

____

____

2.

Number of Songs	Time to Practice
2	8
4	16
6	24

Multiply by 4.

____

____

Put It Together

Write each rule two different ways.

1.

Divide by 8	
Number of Legs	Number of Spiders
72	9
56	7
40	5
24	3
8	1

____

____

2.

Amy's claps	Jordan's claps
1	4
3	6
5	8
7	10

____

____

Find the rule. Use it to find the missing number.

3.

Input	Output
5	12
9	16
13	20
15	?

Rule: ______________________

Number: __________

4.

Input	Output
5	20
6	24
7	28
8	?

Rule: ______________________

Number: __________

Answer the questions. Share your answers with a classmate.

5. Use the table. How many crayons are in 5 boxes? Explain.

Boxes of Crayons	Number of Crayons
4	28
5	?
6	42
7	49

____

6. If Ella has 56 crayons, how many boxes of crayons does she have? Explain.

____

____

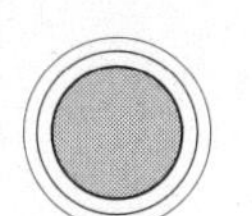

Make It Work

Answer the questions below.

1. Look at the table. What is the rule for the table?

Input	Output
2	10
5	25
7	35
9	45

A. multiply by 5

B. multiply by 8

C. add 8

D. add 5

2. Izzy made a table. The rule for her table is multiply by 4. If the input number is 8, what will the output number be?

A. 4

B. 12

C. 24

D. 32

3. Use the rule to make an input-output table.

Add 6.

Input	Output

____

4. For every 1 cup of orange juice, Lila adds 4 cups of ginger ale to make punch. How many cups of ginger ale will she add if she has 3 cups of orange juice? Explain the rule you used.

____

____

5. Look at the multiplication table. What addition rule could you use to describe the pattern in the column that starts with 3? What column has the same rule? Explain.

	1	2	3	4	5	6	7	8	9	10
1	1	2	3	4	5	6	7	8	9	10
2	2	4	6	8	10	12	14	16	18	20
3	3	6	9	12	15	18	21	24	27	30
4	4	8	12	16	20	24	28	32	36	40
5	5	10	15	20	25	30	35	40	45	50
6	6	12	18	24	30	36	42	48	54	60
7	7	14	21	28	35	42	49	56	63	70
8	8	16	24	32	40	48	56	64	72	80
9	9	18	27	36	45	54	63	72	81	90
10	10	20	30	40	50	60	70	80	90	100

____

____

____

____

Question 1: How many ways can you describe a number?

$5 \times 4 = 20$. $4 \times 5 = 20$. 20 can also be described as 4 groups with 5 marbles in each group or 5 groups with 4 marbles in each group. Or it could be $2 \times 2 \times 5$. There are many different ways to describe a number using multiplication sentences.

Work with a partner to make a list of different ways to describe a number using multiplication. Each of you should write a number at the top of a sheet of paper. Then write one way to describe the number using multiplication. Now, trade your sheets. Write another way to describe the number your partner wrote. Keep going until you can't think of any other ways to write the numbers. Then try with new numbers.

You can also do the same activity using division. Choose a number like 6 and describe it as many ways as you can.

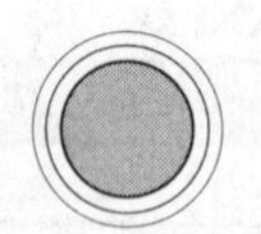

Question 2: What is a fact family?

A great way to remember division and multiplication facts is to remember fact families. Fact families are groups of numbers that are related. To practice your multiplication and division facts using fact families, cut several small pieces of paper. The pieces should be big enough to write four numbers. Choose a fact family and write the three numbers of the fact family on the strip of paper as well as a fourth number that does not belong in the family. Be sure to mix up the numbers.

8	48	5	6

Make at least 5 fact family strips. Then trade your strips with a partner. On each strip, circle the number that does not belong to the fact family. Then write the multiplication and division facts that belong in the fact family.

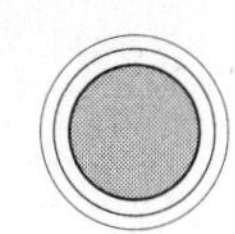

Question 3: Are letters part of math?

Isn't math supposed to use numbers? It does most of the time, but sometimes letters end up in math sentences, too. Letters can be used to represent unknowns in an equation. It is especially helpful to write equations with letters to solve word problems.

Some word problems have one step. Others have two steps. To practice solving multi-step word problems, cut a piece of paper into 20 small pieces, or "cards." Write the letters *a*, *b*, *c*, *d*, *e*, and *f* each on one card. Then write numbers 1 – 10 each on one card. Lastly, write $+$, $-$, $\times$, and $\div$ each on one card. Keep the letters, the numbers, and the operations separate. Now draw two cards from the letter pile, three cards from the number pile, and two cards from the operations pile. Use the letters, the numbers, and the operations to write and solve a word problem with two steps. When you are finished, share your problem with a classmate and describe how you used the letters to help you solve the problem.

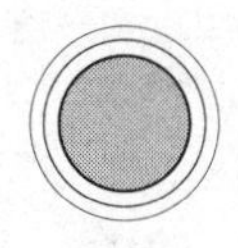

Question 4: How can you use clues to make a pattern?

There are all kinds of patterns in math. Many patterns can be found in addition and multiplication tables. Find a copy of each.

Identify a pattern in one of the tables. Now write a list of clues to help a partner figure out the pattern. For example, the first clue for the pattern "Add 3" might be "Start at the row that begins with 3." The next clue would be a clue that moves your partner closer to figuring out the pattern.

Turn the activity into a game. Make a score sheet. Each person gets a point for every clue needed to figure out the pattern. The person with the least number of points wins!

Rounding Whole Numbers

3.NBT.1 Use place value understanding to round whole numbers to the nearest 10 or 100.

Real World Connections

Key Word

rounded number

Sometimes you don't need to find an exact number. There may have been 512 people at a play, but you could say there were about 500.

A **rounded number** is a number that tells about how many, or that is estimated. It is not exact. You can use place value to help you round whole numbers.

Place Value

When you round a number to the nearest ten, the digit in the ones place becomes 0.

When you round a number to the nearest hundred, the digits in the tens and ones places become 0.

32 = 3 tens, 2 ones **32** rounded to the nearest ten is **30**	**134 = 1 hundred, 3 tens, 4 ones** **134** rounded to the nearest ten is **130** **134** rounded to the nearest hundred is **100**
78 = 7 tens, 8 ones **78** rounded to the nearest ten is **80**	**259 = 2 hundreds, 5 tens, 9 ones** **259** rounded to the nearest ten is **260** **259** rounded to the nearest hundred is **300**

Take It Apart

Follow these steps to round whole numbers to the nearest ten or hundred.

Step 1 Underline the digit in the rounding place. This will be the tens digit if you are rounding to the nearest ten and the hundreds digit if you are rounding to the nearest hundred.

Round 235 to the nearest hundred.

$\underline{2}35$

Step 2 Circle the digit to the right of the digit in the rounding place.

Step 3 If the circled digit is 5 or greater, round up.

If the circled digit is less than 5, round down.

$3 < 5$, so round down.

Round to the nearest hundred.

Step 4 235 rounded to the nearest hundred is 200.

Round each number to the nearest ten.

1. 56 ________
2. 82 ________
3. 428 ________
4. 64 ________
5. 374 ________

Round each number to the nearest hundred.

6. 294 ________
7. 164 ________
8. 514 ________
9. 655 ________
10. 322 ________

Put It Together

Round each number to the place of the underlined digit.

1. $1\underline{5}8$ ______
2. $\underline{8}6$ ______
3. $\underline{3}87$ ______
4. $\underline{1}08$ ______
5. $\underline{6}2$ ______

6. $\underline{4}1$ ______
7. $\underline{9}47$ ______
8. $\underline{7}6$ ______
9. $\underline{5}18$ ______
10. $\underline{4}72$ ______

11. $\underline{5}7$ ______
12. $\underline{9}4$ ______
13. $1\underline{8}2$ ______
14. $6\underline{7}8$ ______
15. $\underline{6}9$ ______

16. $9\underline{0}5$ ______
17. $\underline{3}48$ ______
18. $\underline{1}2$ ______
19. $\underline{6}82$ ______
20. $\underline{3}16$ ______

21. $\underline{2}6$ ______
22. $\underline{6}57$ ______
23. $\underline{2}07$ ______
24. $\underline{7}5$ ______
25. $\underline{2}91$ ______

Answer the questions. Share your ideas with a classmate.

26. There were 922 people at a museum. About how many people were at the museum? Round your answer to the nearest hundred.

____

27. Johanna is thinking of a number with 3 digits. When she rounds her number to the nearest hundred, it is 600. What is a number she could be thinking of? Explain.

____

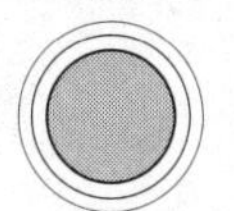

Make It Work

Answer the questions below.

1. Christopher has $284 in his bank account. About how much money does he have in his bank account?

A. about $200

B. about $300

C. about $400

D. about $500

2. Natalie rounds a number up to the nearest ten. What number could be in the ones place?

A. 2

B. 3

C. 4

D. 5

3. There are 84 steps to the top of a tower. About how many steps are there, rounded to the nearest ten?

____

4. Ariana has 204 stickers. About how many stickers does Ariana have? Explain.

____

____

5. Nathaniel has a number of baseball cards that could be rounded by the nearest ten to 350. What is the most baseball cards he could have? Explain how you found your answer.

____

____

____

Using Place Value to Add and Subtract Within 1,000

3.NBT.2 Fluently add and subtract within 1,000 using strategies and algorithms based on place value, properties of operations, and/or the relationship between addition and subtraction.

Real World Connections

Key Words

regroup

sum

Sometimes you need to add larger numbers to solve problems. Imagine there were 543 people at a pool on Saturday and 357 people at the pool on Sunday. How can you find how many people were there on the weekend? You need to add.

One way to add or subtract large numbers is to use place value.

To use place value to add or subtract, line up digits with the same place value.

Write 106 + 48 as
$$\begin{array}{r} 106 \\ +\ \ 48 \\ \hline \end{array}$$

Write 285 − 127 as
$$\begin{array}{r} 285 \\ -\ 127 \\ \hline \end{array}$$

hundreds	tens	ones
	1	
1	0	6
+	4	8
____	5	4

hundreds	tens	ones
	7	15
2	~~8~~	~~5~~
− 1	2	7
____	5	8

Sometimes, you will need to **regroup**, or rename a number. When you add 6 ones and 8 ones, the **sum,** or total, is 14 ones. You cannot write 14 ones in the ones place. Instead, rewrite 14 ones as 1 ten and 4 ones. Then add the 1 ten to the tens column.

You may also need to regroup when you subtract. For example, if you do not have enough ones to subtract from, regroup 1 ten as 10 ones. Remember to subtract 1 ten from the tens column. If you do not have enough tens to subtract from, regroup 1 hundred as 10 tens.

Take It Apart

Follow these steps to add and subtract numbers up to 1,000.

Step 1 Write the problem lining up digits with the same place value.

Step 2 Add or subtract the ones. Regroup 10 ones as 1 ten or 1 ten as 10 ones if you need.

Step 3 Add or subtract the tens. Remember to add or subtract any tens you regrouped. Regroup 10 tens as 1 hundred or 1 hundred as 10 tens if you need.

Step 4 Add or subtract the hundreds. Remember to add or subtract any hundreds you regrouped.

Step 5 Check your answer by adding or subtracting.

	Check		Check
1	5 11	11 1 12 15	1 1
213	7~~6~~~~1~~	~~2~~ ~~2~~ ~~5~~	169
+ 548	− 548	− 56	+ 56
761	213	169	225

Add.

1. 55 + 213
2. 347 + 19
3. 232 + 578
4. 85 + 27
5. 346 + 609

Subtract.

6. 507 − 64
7. 98 − 14
8. 951 − 249
9. 458 − 164
10. 75 − 49

Put It Together

Add or subtract.

1. $517 - 258$

2. $32 + 88$

3. $945 - 651$

4. $354 + 287$

5. $608 - 429$

6. $684 + 58$

7. $205 + 183$

8. $692 - 185$

9. $290 - 82$

10. $480 + 357$

11. $834 - 519$

12. $91 + 67$

13. $773 - 95$

14. $925 + 54$

15. $467 - 392$

16. $81 + 898 =$ ___________

17. $367 - 295 =$ ___________

18. $729 + 118 =$ ___________

19. $500 - 217 =$ ___________

Answer the questions. Share your ideas with a classmate.

20. Martin added $38 + 102 = 140$ to check his subtraction. What could be the subtraction sentence he was checking?

____

21. Alison swam 128 lengths of the pool on Wednesday. She swam 137 lengths of the pool on Thursday. How many lengths of the pool did she swim in all? Explain.

____

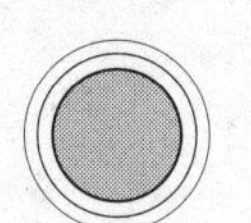

Make It Work

Answer the questions below.

1. Stella has 249 coins in her collection. Her uncle gives her 28 new coins. How many coins does she have now?

A. 221

B. 267

C. 277

D. 278

249
+28
277

2. Erin records the number of cardinals she sees each month in the table.

CARDINALS

Month	Number
May	96
June	132

How many more cardinals did Erin see in June than in May?

A. 36 **B.** 46

C. 64 **D.** 228

132
−96
036

3. Dara saved $225. She bought a bicycle for $189. How much money does she have left?

$36

225
−189
036

4. Jaden read a book with 225 pages last week. He read a book with 167 pages this week. How many pages did he read in all?

392 pages.

225
+167
392

5. Look at the table. Which grade has the smaller number of students? Explain how you found your answer.

Students in Beekman School

Grade	Boys	Girls
Second	126	137
Third	142	128

Boys
126
+137
263

Second grade has less student. I know becaus I added 126+137=263 then. I added 142+128=270. 263 is less then 270.

Girls
142
+128
270

Using Properties of Operations to Add and Subtract Within 1,000

3.NBT.2 Fluently add and subtract within 1,000 using strategies and algorithms based on place value, properties of operations, and/or the relationship between addition and subtraction.

Real World Connections

Key Words

Commutative property of addition

Associative property of addition

Imagine you want to buy a pencil that costs 42¢ and an eraser that costs 45¢. How can you find how much the two items cost in all quickly? You can use different methods and properties of addition to help you find sums and differences faster. These will help you decide if you have enough money to buy the pencil and eraser before you go to the cashier.

Splitting Up Numbers	Rounding
You can split up numbers before you add or subtract. $50 + 38$ $= 50 + (30 + 8)$ $= (50 + 30) + 8$ $= 80 + 8$ $= 88$ $160 - 54$ $= 160 - (50 + 4)$ $= (160 - 50) - 4$ $= 110 - 4$ $= 106$	You can round numbers up or down before adding or subtracting. Add or subtract the difference. $64 + 29$ $= 64 + (30 - 1)$ $= (64 + 30) - 1$ $= 94 - 1$ $= 93$ $64 - 21$ $= 64 - (20 + 1)$ $= (64 - 20) - 1$ $= 44 - 1$ $= 43$
Doubling	**Place Value**
You can double one number when adding two numbers close to each other. Add the difference. $45 + 48$ $= 45 + (45 + 3)$ $= (45 + 45) + 3$ $= 90 + 3$ $= 93$	You can use place value to add or subtract. $236 - 123$ $= (200 + 30 + 6) - (100 + 20 + 3)$ $= (200 - 100) + (30 - 20) + (6 - 3)$ $= 100 + 10 + 3$ $= 113$
Commutative property of addition	**Associative property of addition**
You can add the addends in any order. The sum is the same. $38 + 24 = 24 + 38$	You can group numbers different ways. The sum is the same. Do operations in ( ) first. $(5 + 8) + 3 = 5 + (8 + 3)$ $13 + 3 = 5 + 11$ $16 = 16$

Take It Apart

Follow these steps to help you add and subtract numbers up to 1,000 more quickly.

Step 1 Look for ways to make the addition or subtraction easier.

$120 - 57$

You could split 57 into 50 and 7 or you could round 57 up to 60.

Step 2 Choose a method to help you.

Round 57 to 60.

$120 - (60 - 3)$

Step 3 Add or subtract. Use the properties of addition.

$120 - (60 - 3)$

$= (120 - 60) + 3$

$= 60 + 3$

$= 63$

Choose a method to help you add. Then add.

1. $67 + 70$ 137
2. $45 + 25$ 70
3. $541 + 334$ 875
4. $35 + 18$ 53
5. $249 + 300$ 549

Choose a method to help you subtract. Then subtract.

6. $483 - 271$ 212
7. $98 - 50$ 48
8. $118 - 90$ 28
9. $75 - 48$ 27
10. $524 - 410$ 114

Put It Together

Choose a method to help you add or subtract. Then add or subtract.

1. 214 + 240 = 454

2. 16 + 58 = 74

3. 101 − 58 = 43

4. 220 − 95 = 125

5. 34 + 35 = 69

6. 724 − 513 = 211

7. 72 + 86 = 158

8. 450 − 219 = 231

9. 27 + 30 = 57

10. 84 − 35 = 49

11. 56 + 40 = 96

12. 218 + 361 = 579

13. 108 − 42 = 66

14. 83 + 102 = 185

15. 502 − 298 = 204

16. 148 + 150 = 298

17. 70 − 38 = 32

18. 32 + 70 = 102

19. 304 − 201 = 103

20. 72 + 298 = 370

Answer the questions. Share your ideas with a classmate.

21. There are 418 people in the North bleachers at a basketball game. There are 300 people in the South bleachers. How many people are there in all? Explain.

____

____

____

22. Explain how you can use place value to find the difference between 394 and 282.

____

____

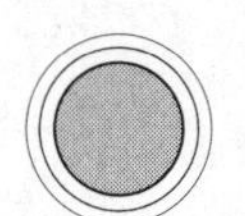

Make It Work

Answer the questions below.

1. Carlos has 48 baseball cards. His friend gives him 50 more baseball cards. How many baseball cards does he have now?

A. 2

B. 98

C. 100

D. 101

2. There were 120 people at a park on Saturday. There were 78 people there on Sunday. How many more people were there on Saturday than on Sunday?

A. 198

B. 58

C. 42

D. 41

3. Angelina has 185 beads. She uses 32 beads to make a bracelet. How many beads does she have left?

____

4. Eli swims for 30 minutes in the morning and for 37 minutes in the afternoon. Choose a method and use it to find out how many minutes he swam in all. Explain why you chose the method.

____

____

____

5. Michael rounds to solve the problem 75 − 22. His answer is 57. Explain what he did wrong.

____

____

____

Lesson 14 Relating Addition and Subtraction

3.NBT.2 Fluently add and subtract within 1,000 using strategies and algorithms based on place value, properties of operations, and/or the relationship between addition and subtraction.

Real World Connections

Key Word

fact family

How can addition help you with subtraction? How can subtraction help you with addition? Addition and subtraction are opposite operations. One undoes the other.

$5 + 6 = 11 \qquad 11 - 6 = 5$

You can use the relationship between addition and subtraction to write fact families. A **fact family** is a group of related addition and subtraction facts that use the same numbers.

Fact Family for 9, 6, and 15	
$9 + 6 = 15$	$15 - 6 = 9$
$6 + 9 = 15$	$15 - 9 = 6$

Fact families can help you solve addition and subtraction problems. If you know one fact in the family, you know all four facts.

You can use addition to check subtraction and subtraction to check addition.

To use addition to check subtraction, start with your answer. Add the number you subtracted. Does your sum equal the number you subtracted from? If so, it is correct.

$$\begin{array}{r} 12 \\ -\ 7 \\ \hline \mathbf{5} \end{array} \qquad \begin{array}{r} \mathbf{5} \\ +\ 7 \\ \hline 12 \end{array}$$

To use subtraction to check addition, start with your answer. Subtract the number you added. Does the difference equal the number you added to? Then you added correctly.

$$\begin{array}{r} 15 \\ +\ 8 \\ \hline \mathbf{23} \end{array} \qquad \begin{array}{r} \mathbf{23} \\ -\ 8 \\ \hline 15 \end{array}$$

Take It Apart

Follow these steps to use addition to help you subtract.

Step 1 Look at the numbers in the problem.

$16 - 7 = \_\_\_\_$

Step 2 Write a related addition sentence.

$\_\_\_\_ + 7 = 16$

Step 3 Complete the addition sentence. Use fact families to help you.

$9 + 7 = 16$

Step 4 Use the addition fact to solve the subtraction problem.

If $9 + 7 = 16$, then $16 - 7 = 9$.

Follow similar steps for using subtraction to help you add.

$8 + 9 = \_\_\_\_$

$\_\_\_\_ - 9 = 8$

$17 - 9 = 8$

$8 + 9 = 17$

Add. Use the subtraction fact to help you.

1. $8 + 6 = \_\_\_\_$

   $14 - 6 = 8$

2. $7 + 6 = \_\_\_\_$

   $13 - 6 = 7$

3. $21 + 7 = \_\_\_\_$

   $28 - 7 = 21$

Subtract. Use the addition fact to help you.

4. $22 - 9 = \_\_\_\_$

   $13 + 9 = 22$

5. $11 - 7 = \_\_\_\_$

   $4 + 7 = 11$

6. $18 - 9 = \_\_\_\_$

   $9 + 9 = 18$

Put It Together

Solve each problem. Use the related fact to help you.

1. $12 - 8 =$ _____
   _____ $+ 8 = 12$

2. $16 - 9 =$ _____
   _____ $+ 9 = 16$

3. $7 + 11 =$ _____
   _____ $- 7 = 11$

4. $15 + 8 =$ _____
   _____ $- 8 = 15$

5. $25 - 12 =$ _____
   _____ $+ 12 = 25$

6. $8 + 12 =$ _____
   _____ $- 12 = 8$

7. $75 + 25 =$ _____
   _____ $- 25 = 75$

8. $60 - 32 =$ _____
   _____ $+ 32 = 60$

9. $35 - 10 =$ _____
   _____ $+ 10 = 35$

10. $250 - 50 =$ ____
    ____ $+ 50 = 250$

11. $45 + 15 =$ _____
    _____ $- 15 = 45$

12. $24 + 9 =$ _____
    _____ $- 9 = 24$

Answer the questions. Share your ideas with a classmate.

13. Ethan writes $34 + 19 = 53$. Write a subtraction problem he can do to check his answer.

____

14. Adriana has 14 bananas. She puts 6 bananas in a basket. How many bananas does she have left? Explain how you can use an addition fact to help you.

____

____

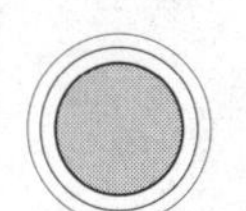

Make It Work

Answer the questions below.

1. Annabeth adds 14 + 18 to get a sum of 32. Which fact could she use to check her answer?

A. 14 + 32 = 46

B. 14 × 18 = 252

C. 32 + 18 = 50

D. 32 − 18 = 14

2. Caleb has 22 crystals in his collection. His sister gives him some more rocks. Now he has 30 crystals. How many crystals did his sister give him?

A. 6

B. 8

C. 64

D. 52

3. Mackenzie wrote 12 thank you cards before lunch and 6 thank you cards after lunch. How many thank you cards did she write in all?

____

4. Dominic puts 15 pencils on the table. His brother takes 6 of them. How many pencils are on the table now?

Solve | Check

5. Nevaeh moved forward 8 spaces in a game. Then she moved back 4 spaces. Then she moved forward 4 spaces. Where is she compared to where she started? Use your answer to explain how addition is the opposite of subtraction.

Lesson 15 Multiplying by Multiples of 10

3.NBT.3 Multiply one-digit whole numbers by multiples of 10 in the range 10–90 (e.g., 9×80, 5×60) using strategies based on place value and properties of operations.

Real World Connections

Key Word

basic multiplication facts

There are 8 classes of first grade students at Washington Elementary. Each class has 20 students. How can you find the total number of first graders?

You need to multiply 8×20 to find the total number of first graders.

20 is a multiple of 10. $2 \times 10 = 20$. Other multiples of 10 are 30, 40, 50, 60, 70, 80, and 90.

You can use **basic multiplication facts** to help you multiply by multiples of 10. Basic multiplication facts are all the multiplication facts up to 10×10, like 4×3, 2×6, and 8×9.

When you multiply by a multiple of 10, rewrite the multiple of ten as a number of tens.

$$20 = 2 \text{ tens}$$

$$8 \times 20 = 8 \times 2 \text{ tens}$$

$$= 16 \text{ tens}$$

$$= 16 \times 10$$

$$= 160$$

When you multiply by any multiple of 10, multiply the basic fact and place a zero after it.

$$8 \times 20 = ?$$

$$8 \times 2 = 16$$

$$\text{So } 8 \times 2\mathbf{0} = 16\mathbf{0}$$

Take It Apart

Follow these steps to multiply by multiples of 10.

Step 1 Use place value to regroup the multiple of ten. Write it as a number of tens.

4×30

$30 = 3$ tens

So $4 \times 30 = 4 \times 3$ tens

Step 2 Use basic facts to find how many tens.

$4 \times 3 = 12$

So 4×3 tens $= 12$ tens

Step 3 Write the number of tens as a whole number.

12 tens $= 12 \times 10 = 120$

So $4 \times 30 = 120$

Multiply.

1. $9 \times 40 = 9 \times$ ______ tens

   = ______ tens

   = ______

2. $5 \times 60 = 5 \times$ ______ tens

   = ______ tens

   = ______

3. $3 \times 50 = 3 \times$ ______ tens

   = ______ tens

   = ______

4. $8 \times 90 = 8 \times$ ______ tens

   = ______ tens

   = ______

5. $6 \times 30 = 6 \times$ ______ tens

   = ______ tens

   = ______

6. $7 \times 40 = 7 \times$ ______ tens

   = ______ tens

   = ______

Put It Together

Multiply.

1. $5 \times 10 =$ __________ **2.** $8 \times 40 =$ __________ **3.** $6 \times 40 =$ __________

4. $3 \times 70 =$ __________ **5.** $5 \times 70 =$ __________ **6.** $8 \times 80 =$ __________

7. $4 \times 20 =$ __________ **8.** $2 \times 80 =$ __________ **9.** $9 \times 70 =$ __________

10. $4 \times 80 =$ __________ **11.** $3 \times 60 =$ __________ **12.** $4 \times 50 =$ __________

13. $6 \times 70 =$ __________ **14.** $7 \times 90 =$ __________ **15.** $8 \times 70 =$ __________

16. $3 \times 80 =$ __________ **17.** $2 \times 90 =$ __________ **18.** $4 \times 90 =$ __________

Answer the questions. Share your ideas with a classmate.

19. Which basic fact can you use to find the product of 60×4?

____

20. There are 6 rows of bleachers at the pool. Each row fits 30 people. How many people can sit on the pool bleachers? Explain how you solved the problem.

____

____

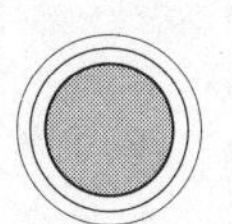

Make It Work

Answer the questions below.

1. A store sold 20 puzzles each day for 5 days. Which basic multiplication fact can you use to find how many puzzles they sold in all?

A. $5 \times 2 = 10$

B. $2 \times 10 = 20$

C. $5 \times 10 = 50$

D. $5 \times 12 = 60$

2. A car is driving 60 miles per hour. How many miles can the car drive in 5 hours?

A. 30 miles

B. 60 miles

C. 300 miles

D. 600 miles

3. Miguel has 4 twenty-dollar bills. How much money does he have?

____

4. Dakota put 20 paintbrushes on each of 6 tables for her art class. How many paintbrushes are there in all? Show your work.

____

5. Eliza can type 50 words a minute. Jonathan can type 60 words a minute. How many more words can Jonathan type than Eliza in 7 minutes? Explain.

____

____

____

Chapter 2

Question 1: When is it useful to round numbers?

You round numbers when you don't need an exact number. You probably don't need to know exactly how many people are at a baseball game – just about how many people are there.

Rounding numbers can be useful when you are traveling. People who travel by car often use maps to find how far it is from place to place. Many maps have numbers next to roads showing how many miles it is between two points on the map.

Rennville ———— 62 ———— Cascade Falls

Make a map on a sheet of paper. It can be a map of actual places or places you create. List mileage between places. Include numbers that can be rounded to the nearest ten or hundred. Then write at least 3 questions about distances on your map, such as "About how many miles is it from Point A to Point B?" Trade your map with a partner and answer your partner's questions.

Question 2: How can you describe how to use place value to add and subtract?

It is important to understand how to use place value when you add and subtract larger numbers. In addition, you may need to regroup 10 ones as 1 ten or 10 tens as 1 hundred. In subtraction, you may need to regroup 1 hundred as 10 tens or 1 ten as 10 ones.

Work with a partner to write an addition problem that involves regrouping both ones and tens. Create a short presentation in which you describe how to regroup. How can you best help other students to understand regrouping? Do you want to use objects to represent ones and tens? Do you have another strategy to help them see how the tens and ones are regrouped? When you are finished, give your presentation to the class.

Question 3: Is there more than one way to add or subtract?

There are lots and lots of ways to add or subtract. It really doesn't matter how you work an addition or subtraction problem as long as you get to the correct answer!

Make a memory game using addition and subtraction problems and different ways to solve them. For example, the match for $30 + 33$ might be $30 + (30 + 3)$ or the match for $28 + 57$ might be $28 + (60 - 3)$. Be creative. Use the strategies you know to write different and challenging matches. Then play your game with a partner.

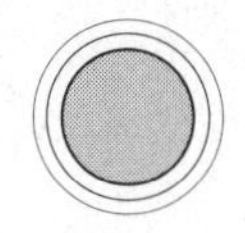

Question 4: How can you find products without multiplying?

You can use different strategies to multiply. When you multiply any number by ten, you don't need to multiply, just add a zero to the number. $8 \times 10 = 80$. You can use a similar trick when multiplying by multiples of ten. Multiply the number by the first digit of the ten, then add a zero. $3 \times 80 = 240$. If you know 3×8, you know 3×80. If you know 7×5, you know 7×50.

Make a Multiply by Multiples Robot. Use materials you have, like paper or cardboard, to create your robot. Ask classmates to ask the robot to solve problems with multiples of ten. Then answer your classmates using your best robot voice!

Lesson 16 Understanding Fractions

3.NF.1 Understand a fraction $\frac{1}{b}$ as the quantity formed by 1 part when a whole is partitioned into b equal parts; understand a fraction $\frac{a}{b}$ as the quantity formed by a parts of size $\frac{1}{b}$.

Real World Connections

Key Words
- fraction
- numerator
- denominator

Bae Lin's art teacher asks her to fold a sheet of paper into 4 equal parts. What part of the whole sheet of paper is one part?

When you divide a whole into equal parts, you can describe the parts as fractions. A **fraction** is a number that names equal parts of a whole.

A fraction has a numerator and a denominator. The **numerator** is the number of parts you are counting. The **denominator** is the total number of equal parts in the whole.

There are 4 equal parts. The square is divided into fourths. One part is shaded. The shaded part is $\frac{1}{4}$.

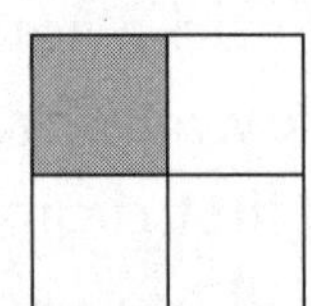

1 ← numerator
4 ← denominator

one fourth

There are 4 equal parts. Three parts are shaded. The shaded part is $\frac{3}{4}$.

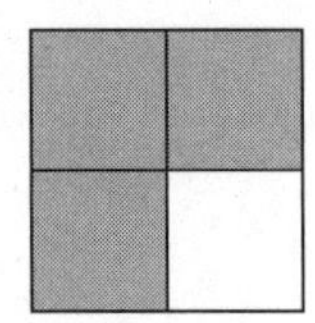

3 ← numerator
4 ← denominator

three-fourths

Take It Apart

To write fractions of a whole or a group, follow these steps.

Step 1 Count the number of equal parts in the whole or group.
This is the denominator.

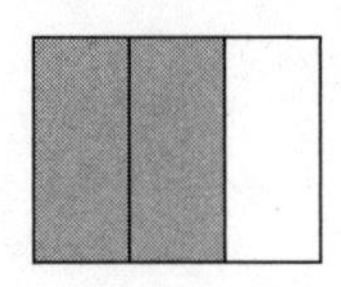

There are 3 equal parts.

Step 2 Count the number of parts being considered. This is the numerator.

Two of the parts are shaded.

Step 3 Write the fraction.

$\frac{2}{3}$ ← numerator / ← denominator

Complete the fraction that names the shaded part.

1. 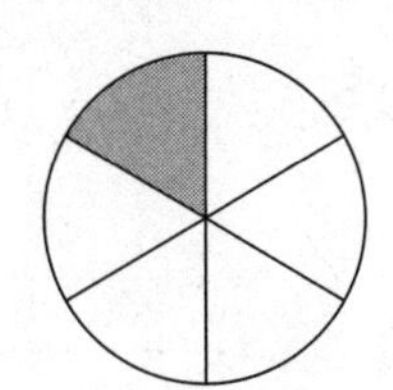

$\frac{\ }{6}$

2. 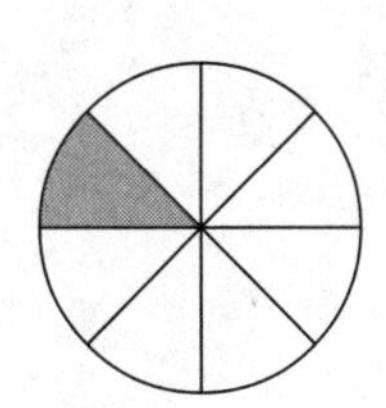

$\frac{\ }{8}$

3. 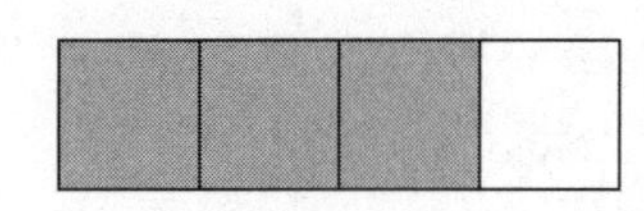

$\frac{\ }{4}$

4. 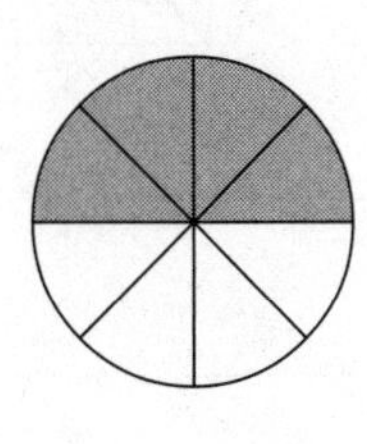

$\frac{4}{\ }$

5. 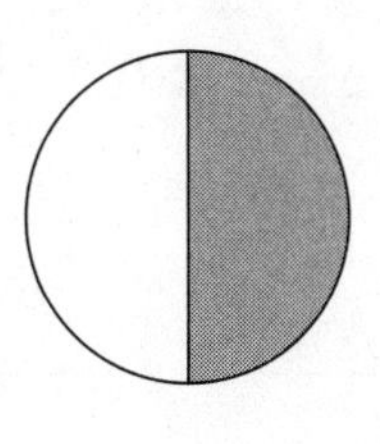

$\frac{1}{\ }$

6. 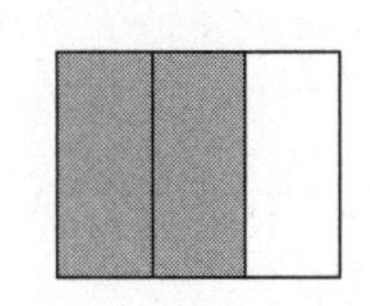

$\frac{2}{\ }$

Put It Together

Write the fraction for the shaded part.

1. 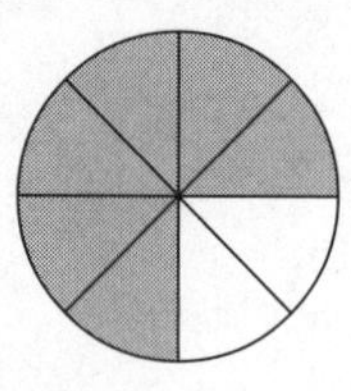 ____

2. 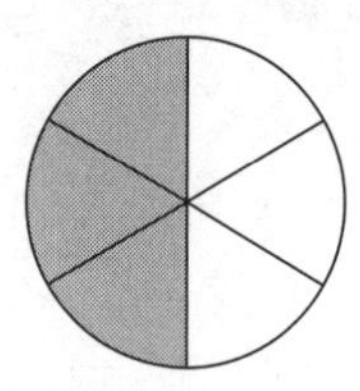 ____

3. 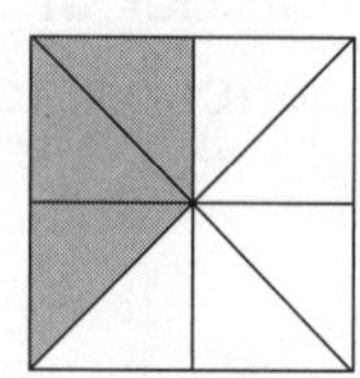 ____

4. 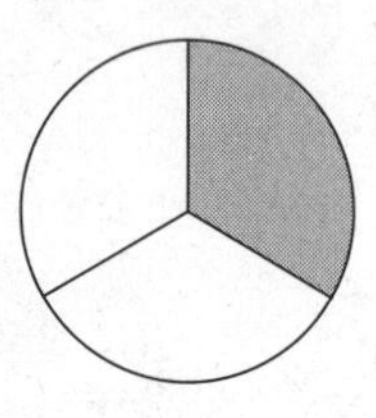 ____

5. 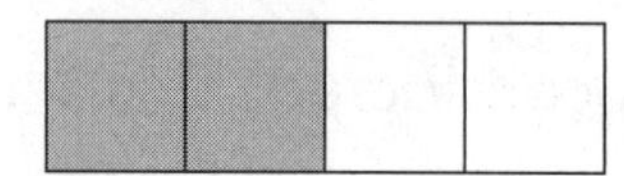 ____

6. 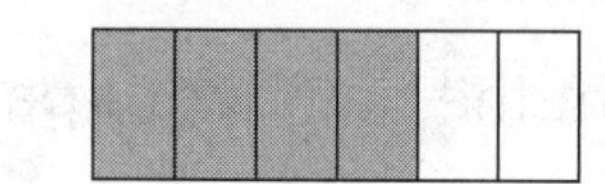 ____

Answer the questions. Share your ideas with a classmate.

7. Delaney divides a sandwich into four equal pieces. She eats 2 of the pieces. What fraction of her sandwich did she eat?

____

8. Samuel is not sure what three-fourths means. Shade the square to show three-fourths. Then explain how the picture shows three-fourths.

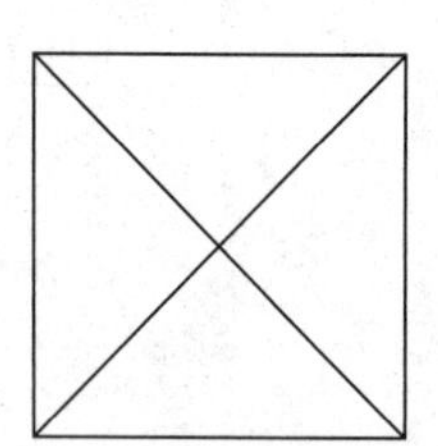

____

____

____

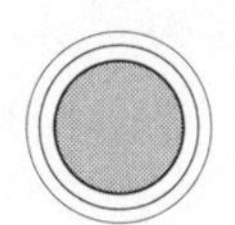

Make It Work

Answer the questions below.

1. Tess decorated her wall with different kinds of wallpaper. What fraction of the wall has stripes?

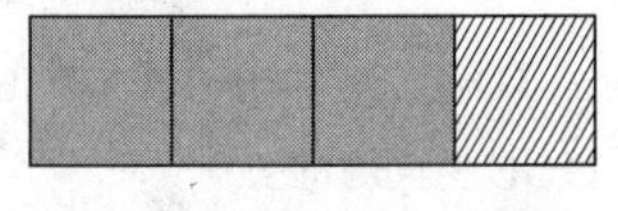

A. $\frac{3}{4}$ **B.** $\frac{2}{4}$

C. $\frac{1}{2}$ **D.** $\frac{1}{4}$

2. Adam divided an orange into 8 equal pieces. He gave 5 of the pieces to his sister. What fraction of the orange did he give to his sister?

A. $\frac{1}{8}$ **B.** $\frac{3}{8}$

C. $\frac{5}{8}$ **D.** $\frac{7}{8}$

3. What fraction of the circle is shaded?

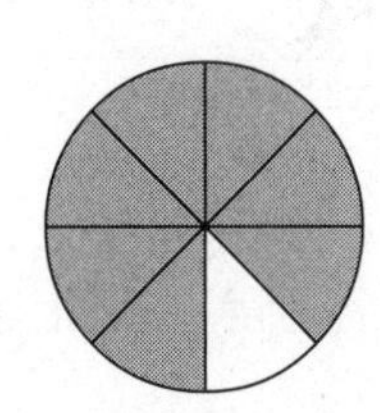

______

4. Shade the figure to show $\frac{5}{6}$.

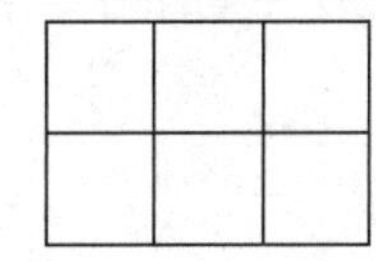

5. Jesse divides a veggie pizza into 8 equal pieces. He eats 2 pieces and his brother eats 2 pieces. What fraction of the pizza is left? Explain.

____

____

____

Understanding Fractions on Number Lines

3.NF.2.a Represent a fraction $\frac{1}{b}$ on a number line diagram by defining the interval from 0 to 1 as the whole and partitioning it into b equal parts. Recognize that each part has size $\frac{1}{b}$ and that the endpoint of the part based at 0 locates the number $\frac{1}{b}$ on the number line.

Real World Connections

Key Word

fraction

Tristan is having difficulty understanding fractions. A **fraction** describes part of a whole. What is another way you can show fractions to help Tristan understand them?

You can show fractions on a number line. You can divide the distance between 0 and 1 on a number line into equal parts.

This number line is divided into 4 equal parts. It is divided into fourths.

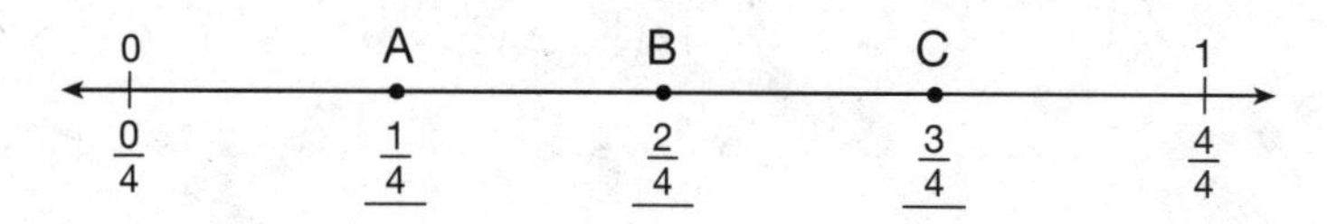

Each equal part on the number line is $\frac{1}{4}$.

Where is the fraction $\frac{1}{4}$ on the number line?

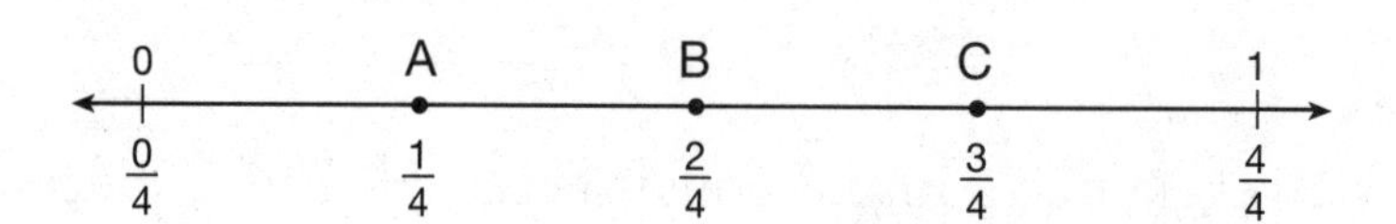

$\frac{1}{4}$ is the point that is one equal part from 0, which is point A.

Take It Apart

To represent a fraction on a number line, follow these steps.

Step 1 Look at the denominator of the fraction. This tells you into how many equal parts you will divide the number line. Divide the distance between 0 and 1 into equal parts.

To show $\frac{1}{2}$ on a number line, divide the distance between 0 and 1 into 2 equal parts because the denominator is 2.

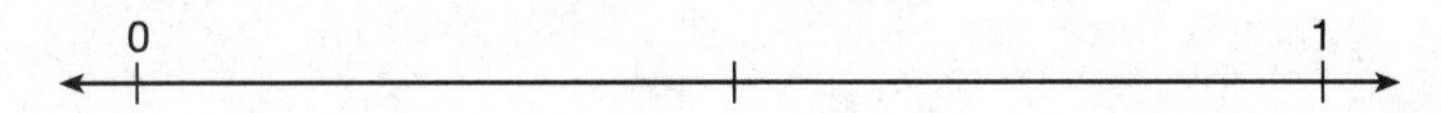

Step 2 Start at 0. Move one space to the right. This point represents $\frac{1}{b}$, where b is the number of spaces between 0 and 1.

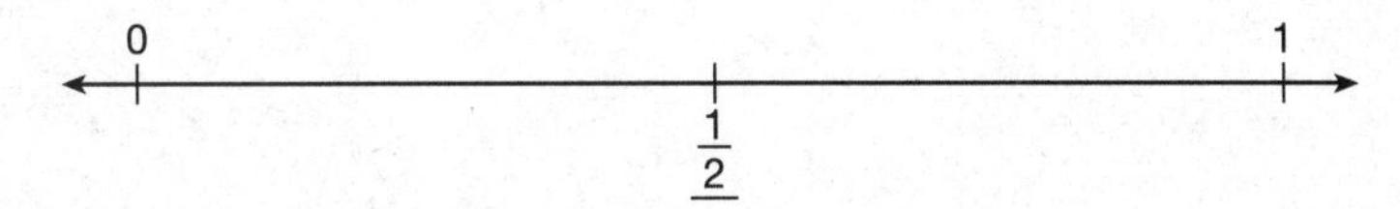

Write the fraction represented by point A on each number line.

1.

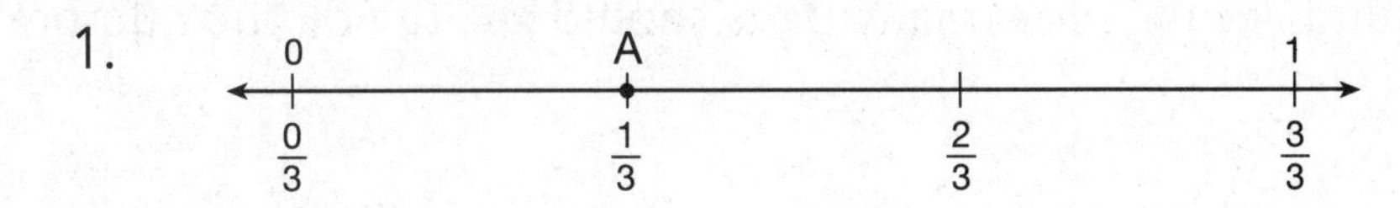

______

2.

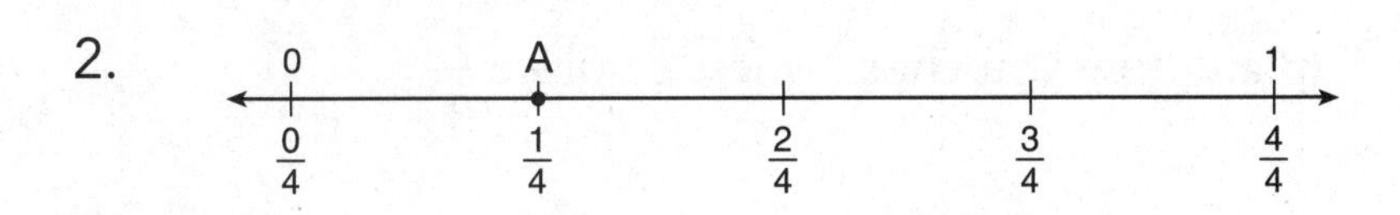

______

3.

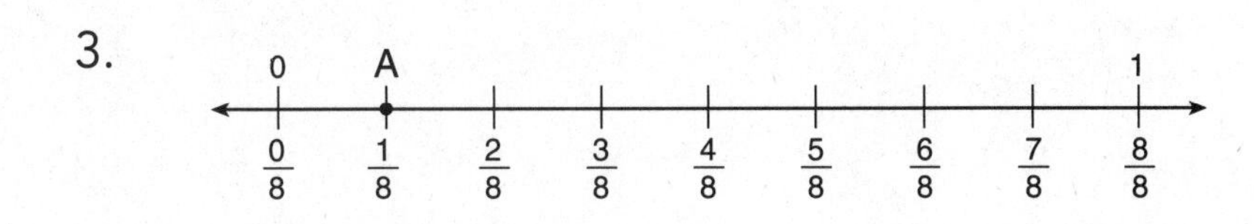

______

4.

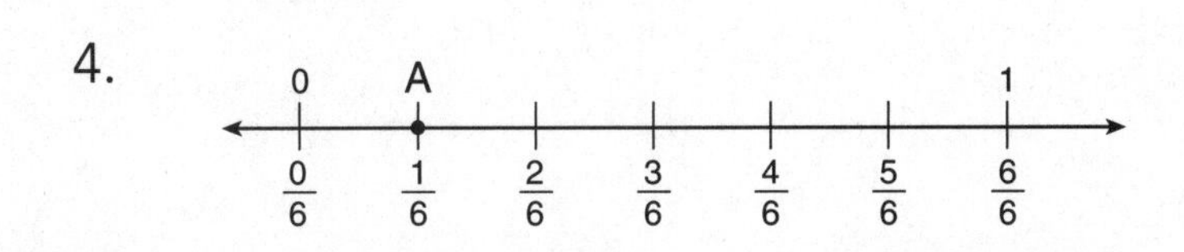

______

Put It Together

Find and label each fraction on the number line.

1. $\frac{1}{4}$

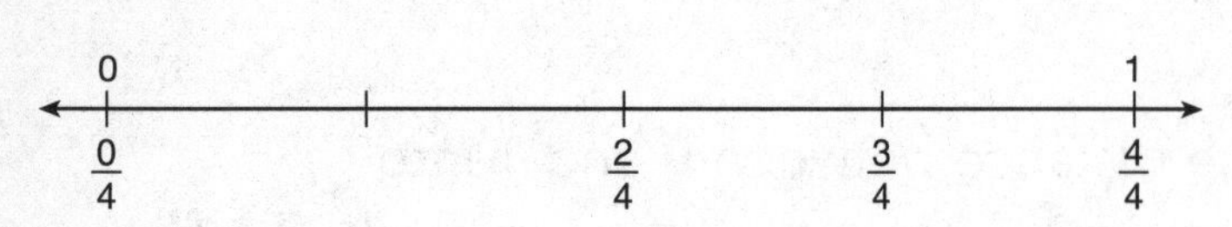

2. $\frac{1}{6}$

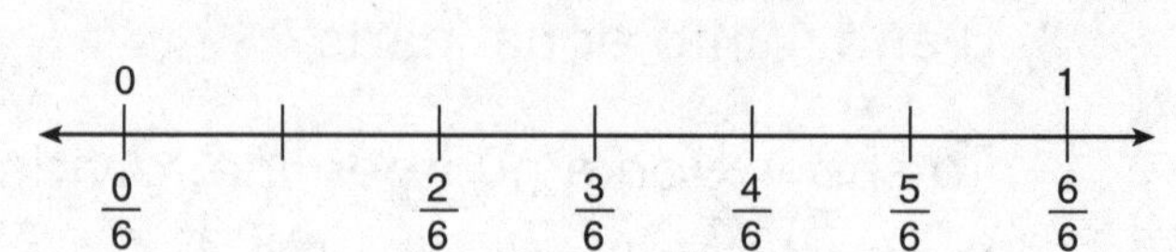

3. $\frac{1}{3}$

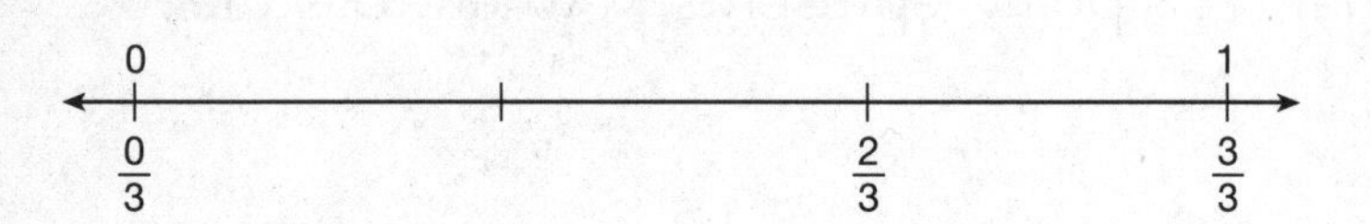

4. $\frac{1}{2}$

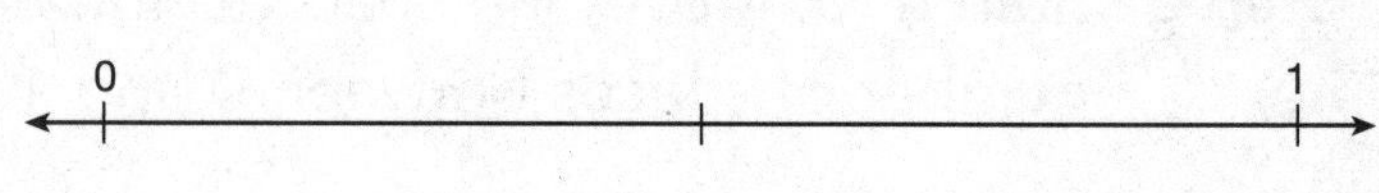

Answer the questions. Share your ideas with a classmate.

5. Mira wants to show $\frac{1}{8}$ on a number line. How many parts should she divide the number line into between 0 and 1? Explain.

____

____

6. Show $\frac{1}{6}$ on the number line. Explain how you chose where to place $\frac{1}{6}$.

____

____

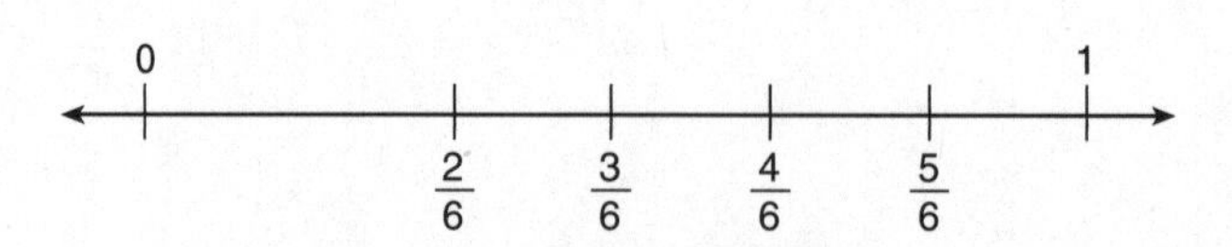

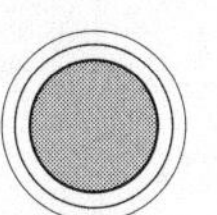

Make It Work

Answer the questions below.

1. The distance between Taya's school and her home is 1 mile.

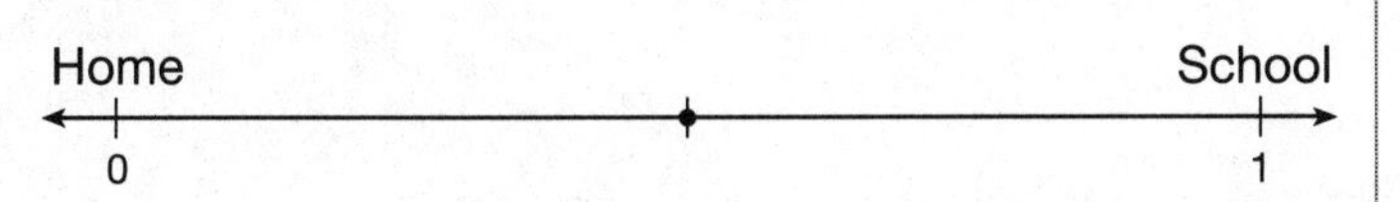

What fraction represents the halfway point between home and school?

A. $\frac{1}{2}$

B. $\frac{1}{3}$

C. $\frac{1}{4}$

D. $\frac{1}{5}$

2. Freddy wants to show $\frac{1}{6}$ on a number line. Which shows how he divides the number line?

A. 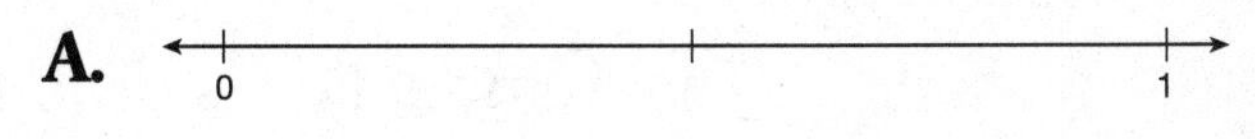

B. 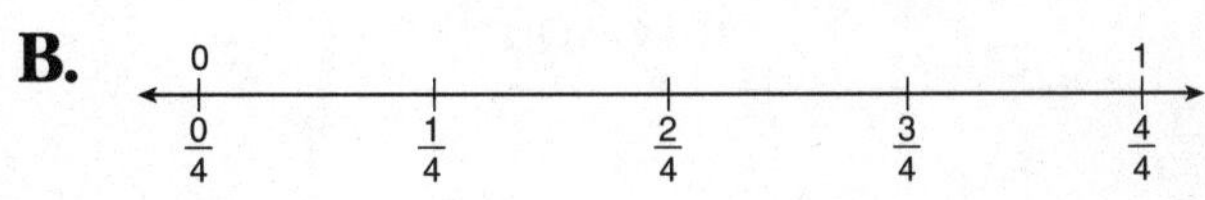

C. 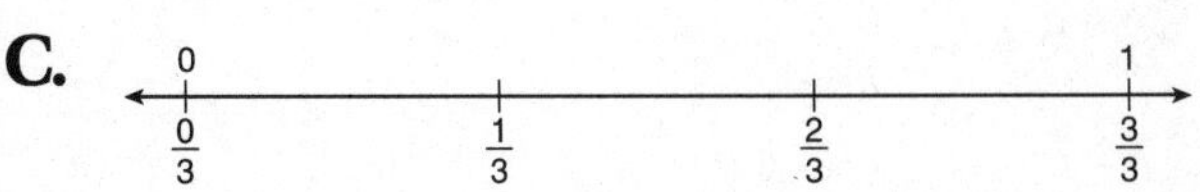

D. 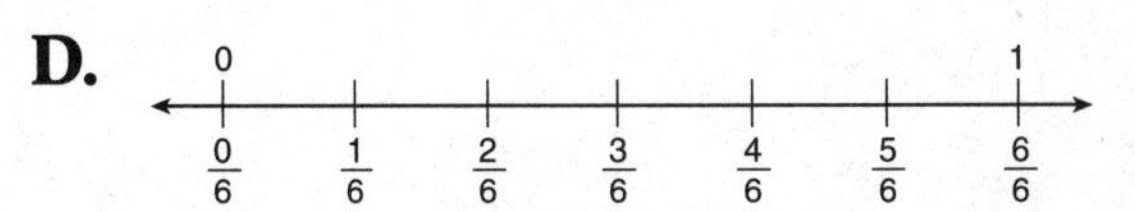

3. What fraction is represented by point A?

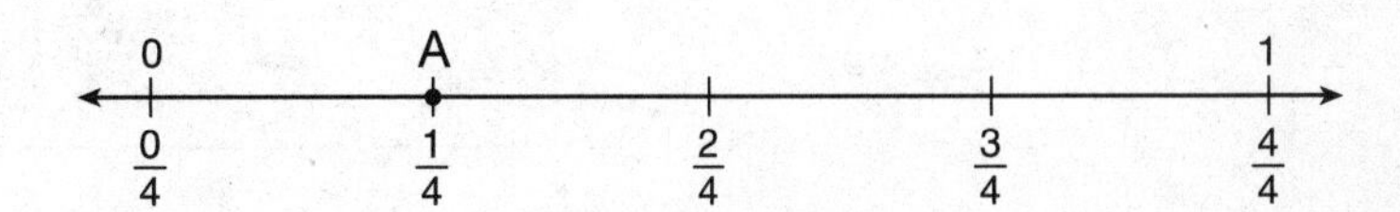

______

4. Otto says that point A represents $\frac{1}{4}$. Valerie says it represents $\frac{1}{8}$. Who is correct? Explain.

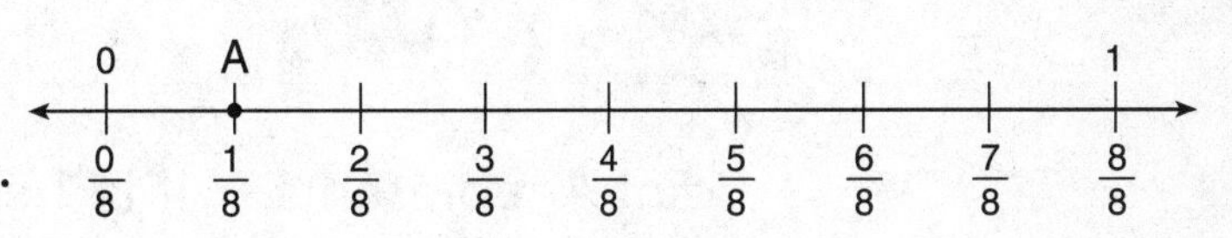

____

____

____

5. Victoria shares $\frac{1}{8}$ of the apple pie she baked with her brother. Draw a number line to show $\frac{1}{8}$. Explain how you know where $\frac{1}{8}$ is on the number line.

____

____

____

Representing Fractions on Number Lines

3.NF.2.b Represent a fraction $\frac{a}{b}$ on a number line diagram by marking off a lengths $\frac{1}{b}$ from 0. Recognize the resulting interval has size $\frac{a}{b}$ and that its endpoint locates the number $\frac{a}{b}$ on the number line.

Real World Connections

Key Word

fraction

What is another way to show fractions with numerators other than 1?

You can use a number line to show any fraction. A **fraction** describes part of a whole.

This number line is divided into 4 equal parts. It is divided into fourths.

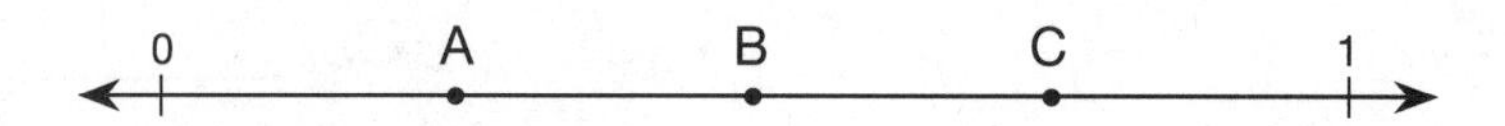

What fractions are represented by points A, B, and C?

Each space on the number line is equal to $\frac{1}{4}$.

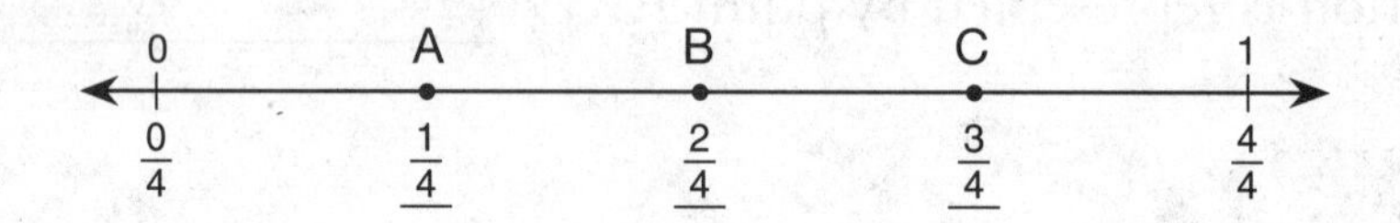

Point A represents $\frac{1}{4}$. It is 1 space, or one-fourth, from 0.

Point B represents $\frac{2}{4}$. It is 2 spaces, or two-fourths, from 0.

Point C represents $\frac{3}{4}$. It is 3 spaces, or three-fourths, from 0.

Take It Apart

To represent a fraction on a number line, follow these steps.

Step 1 Divide the distance between 0 and 1 into equal parts. The number of equal parts is the same as the denominator of the fraction.

To represent $\frac{3}{4}$ on a number line, divide the number line into 4 equal parts.

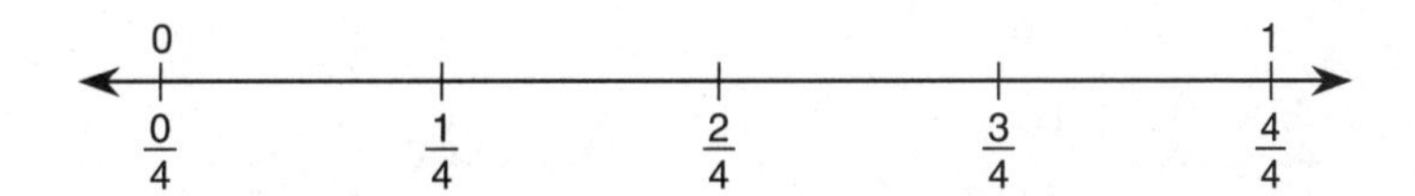

Look at the number in the numerator of the fraction you want to show. This tells you how many spaces to move from 0.

The numerator in $\frac{3}{4}$ is 3, so move 3 spaces to the right.

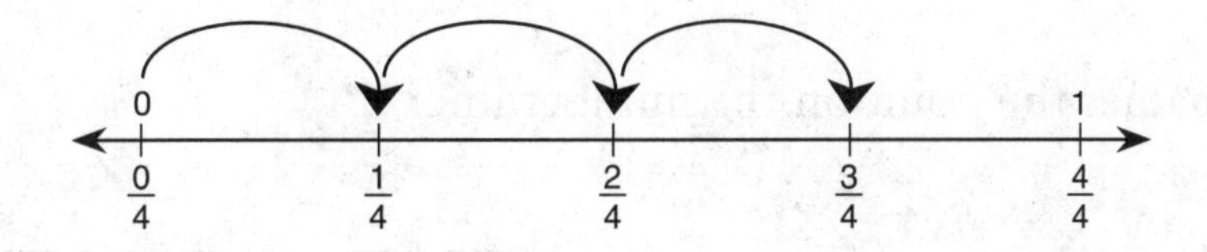

Use the number line. Write the point name for each missing fraction on the number line.

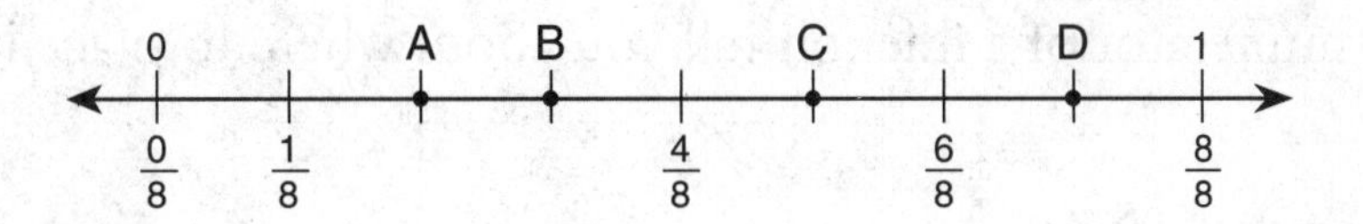

1. $\frac{3}{8}$ ______________

2. $\frac{7}{8}$ ______________

3. $\frac{5}{8}$ ______________

4. $\frac{2}{8}$ ______________

Put It Together

Draw a dot and label each point on the number line.

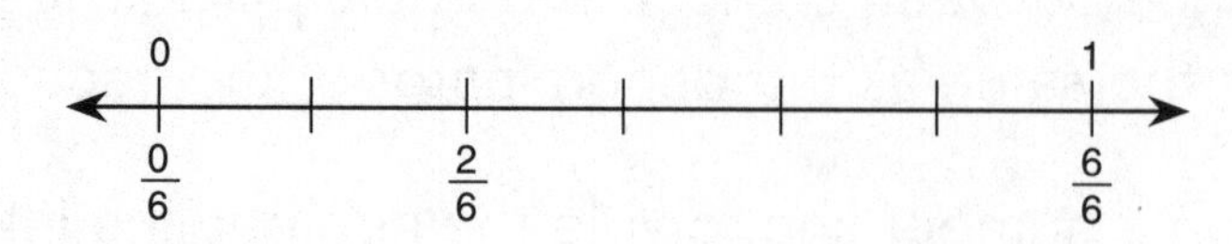

1. P at $\frac{3}{6}$ **2.** R at $\frac{1}{6}$ **3.** S at $\frac{4}{6}$ **4.** T at $\frac{5}{6}$

5. What fraction names the point on the number line?

____

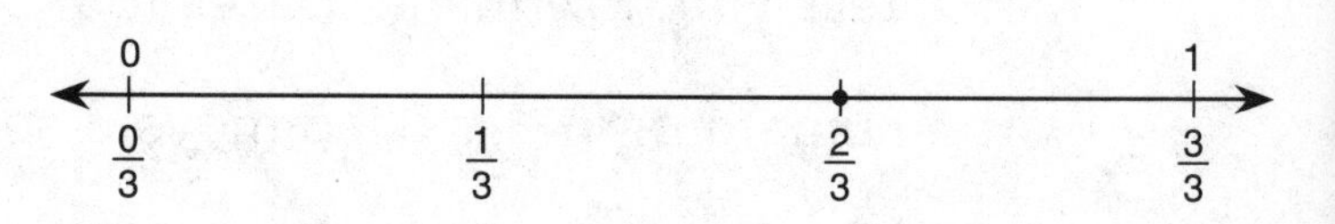

6. What fraction names the point on the number line?

____

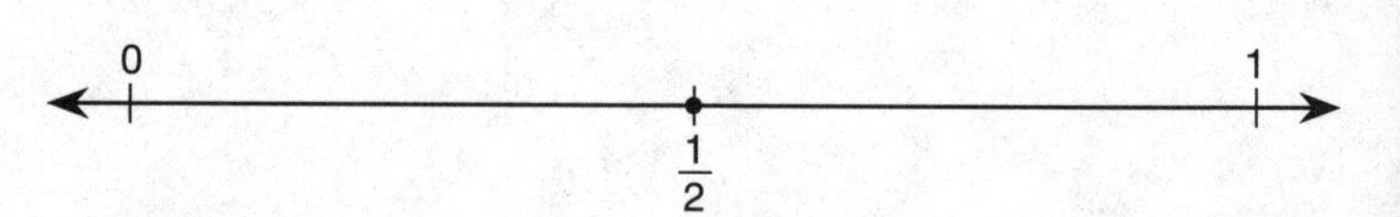

Answer the questions. Share your ideas with a classmate.

7. What does the numerator of a fraction tell you about where to place it on a number line?

____

____

8. Isaac represented a fraction on a number line. The fraction was between 0 and 1. What must be true about the numerator of the fraction compared to the denominator?

____

____

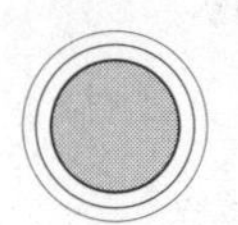

Make It Work

Answer the questions below.

1. Which point best represents $\frac{5}{6}$ on the number line?

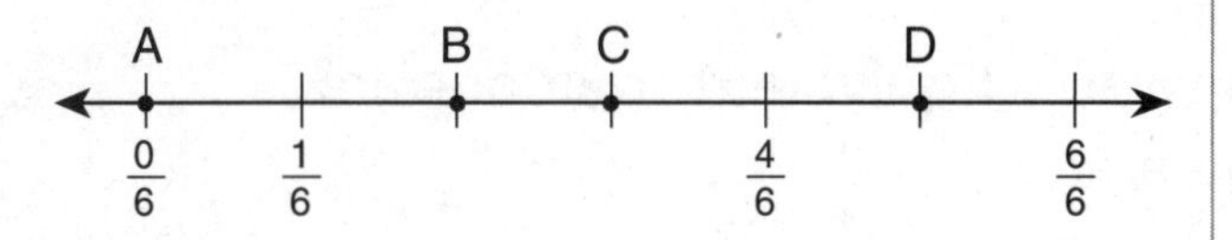

A. point A **B.** point B

C. point C **D.** point D

2. Which fraction represents point Q on the number line?

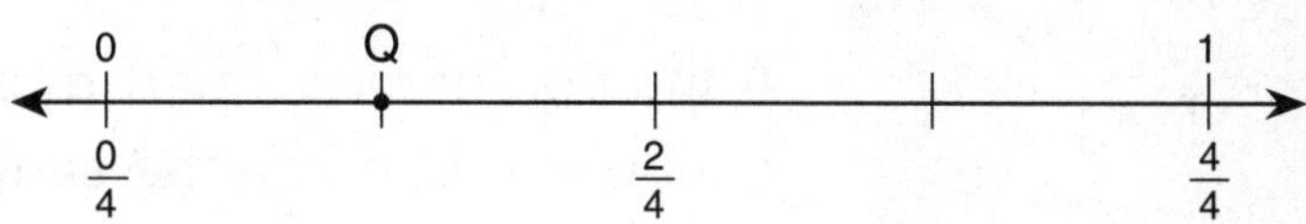

A. $\frac{0}{4}$ **B.** $\frac{1}{4}$

C. $\frac{2}{4}$ **D.** $\frac{3}{4}$

Use the diagram for questions 3 and 4.

3. How far is it from Chase's house to the school?

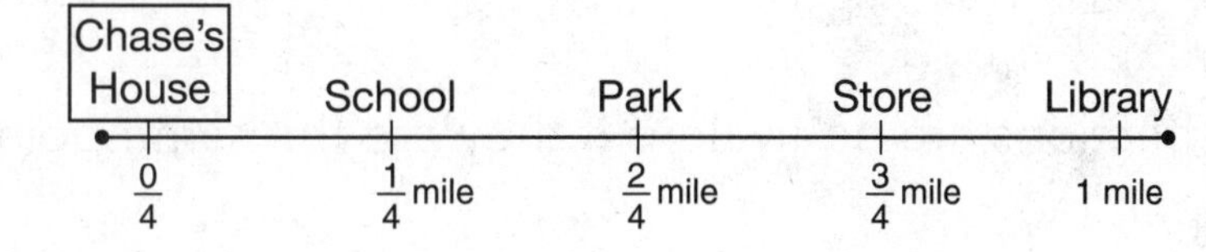

____

4. Chase starts at his house and walks $\frac{2}{4}$ of a mile. Where is he now? Explain.

____

5. Elizabeth measured the width of a square button using an inch ruler. How wide is her button? Explain.

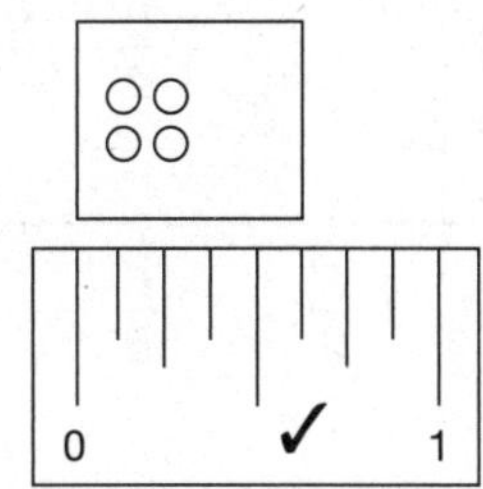

____

____

____

Understanding Equivalent Fractions

3.NF.3.a Understand two fractions as equivalent (equal) if they are the same size, or the same point on a number line.

Real World Connections

Key Word

equivalent fractions

Clara divided a pizza into sixths. She ate one half of the pizza. How many sixths of the pizza did she eat?

A fraction names a part of a whole. **Equivalent fractions** are fractions that name the same amount.

Two fractions are equivalent if they are the same size.

$\frac{1}{2}$			$\frac{1}{2}$		
$\frac{1}{6}$	$\frac{1}{6}$	$\frac{1}{6}$	$\frac{1}{6}$	$\frac{1}{6}$	$\frac{1}{6}$

$$\frac{1}{2} = \frac{3}{6}$$

Two fractions are equivalent if they are the same point on a number line.

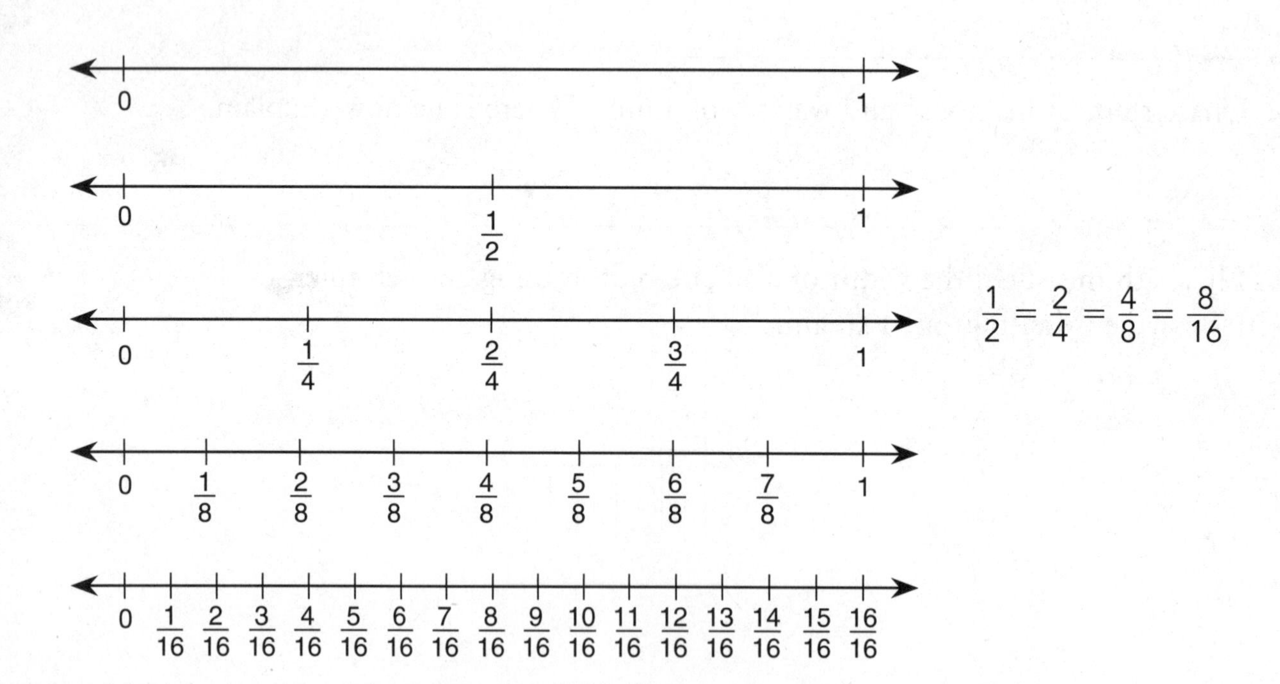

Take It Apart

Follow these steps to decide if two fractions are equivalent.

Step 1 Look at or draw models of the two fractions or locate the fractions on a number line.

Step 2 Are the two fractions the same size? If so, they are equivalent.

Are the two fractions at the same point on the number line? If so, they are equivalent.

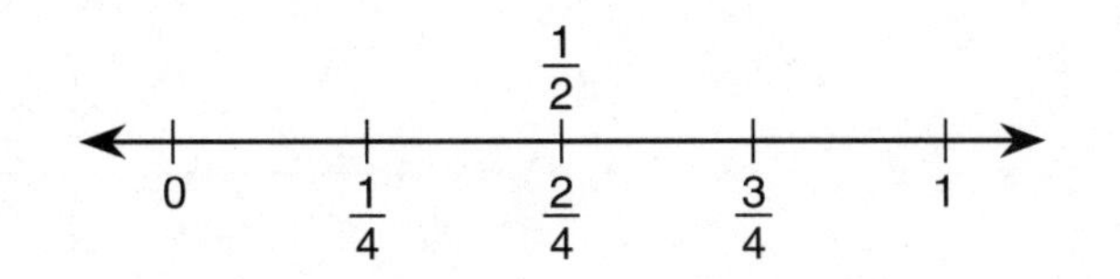

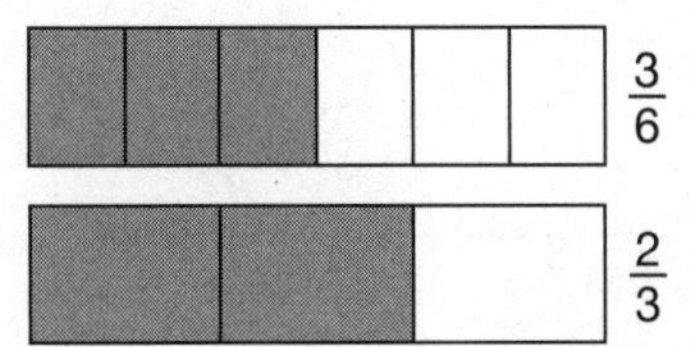

$\frac{1}{2}$ is equivalent to $\frac{2}{4}$.

$\frac{3}{6}$ is not equivalent to $\frac{2}{3}$.

Are the fractions equivalent? Write *yes* or *no*.

1. 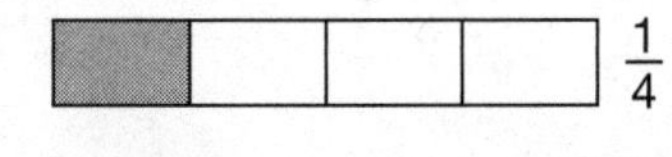

____

2. 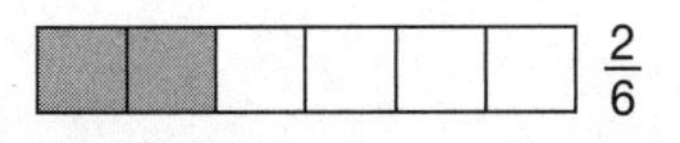

____

3. 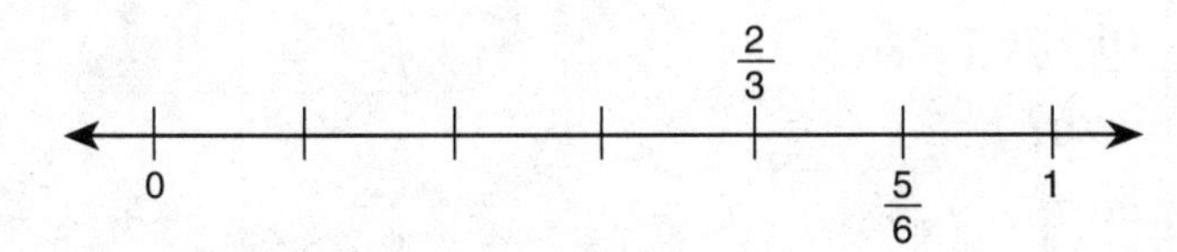

____

4. 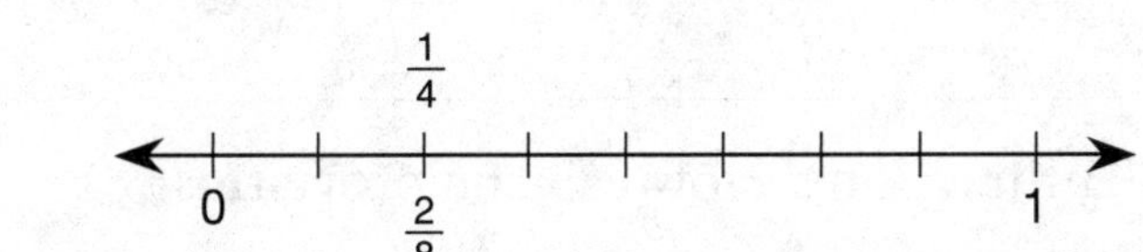

____

Put It Together

Are the fractions equivalent? Write *yes* or *no*.

1.

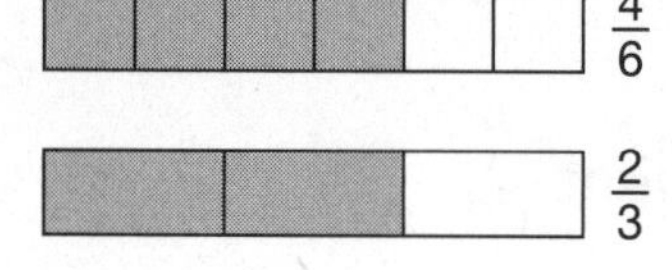

______

2.

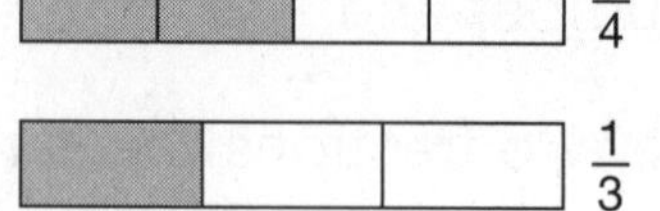

______

3.

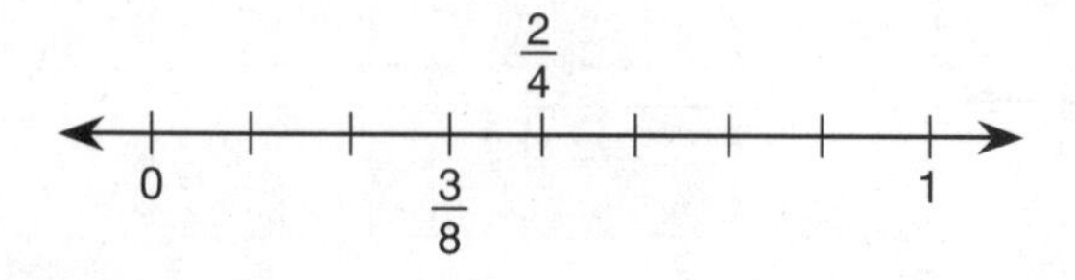

______

4.

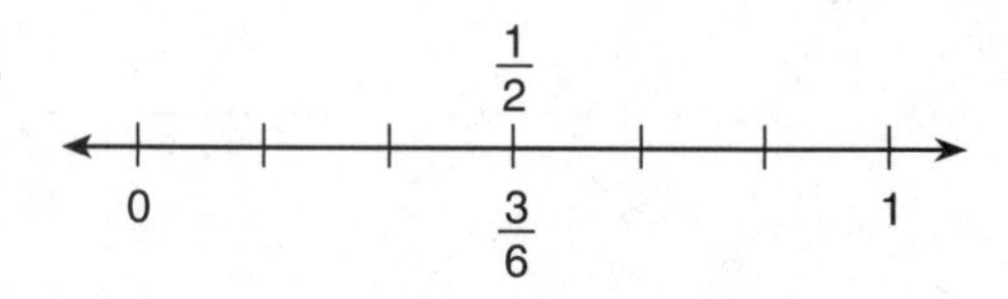

______

5.

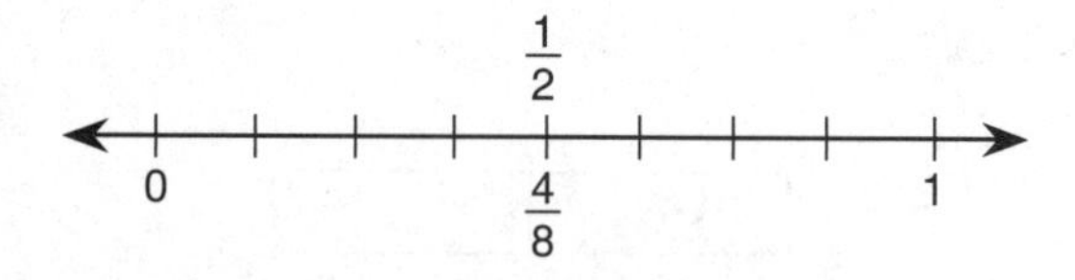

______

6.

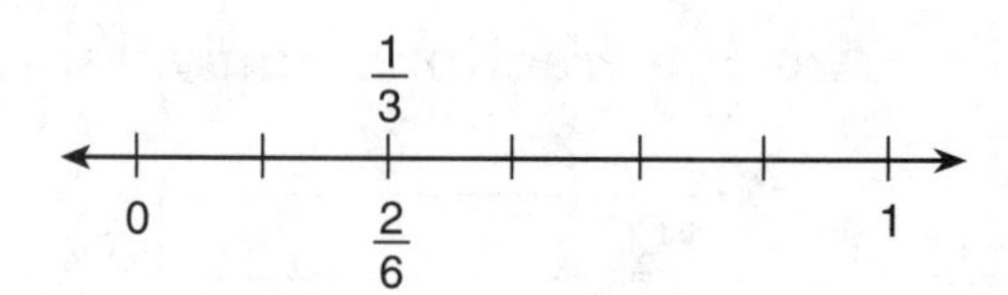

______

Answer the questions. Share your ideas with a classmate.

7. Albert ate $\frac{1}{4}$ of a pizza. James ate $\frac{3}{8}$ of the pizza. Did they eat the same amount of pizza? Shade the models to help you. Explain.

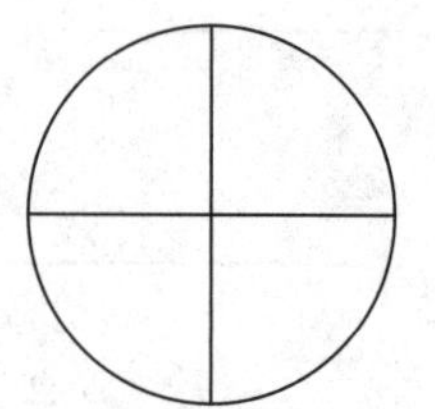

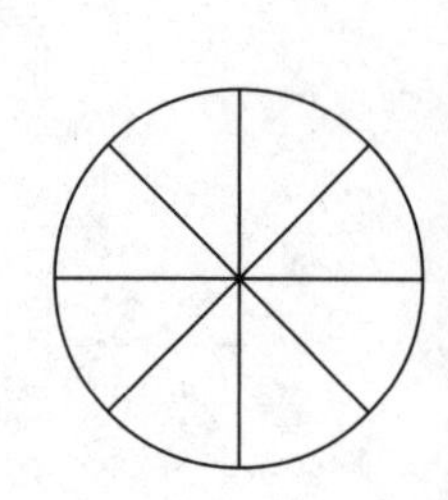

____

____

8. Eliana believes that $\frac{1}{2}$ and $\frac{4}{8}$ are equivalent fractions. How can she prove this?

____

____

____

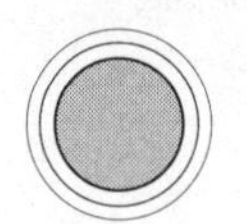

Make It Work

Answer the questions below.

1. Which figure shows a fraction equivalent to $\frac{1}{4}$?

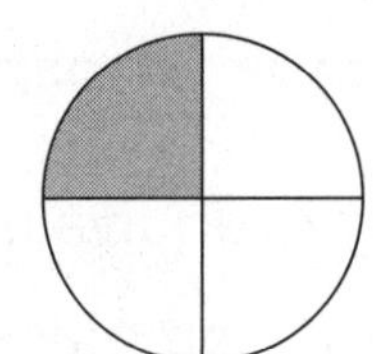

A. 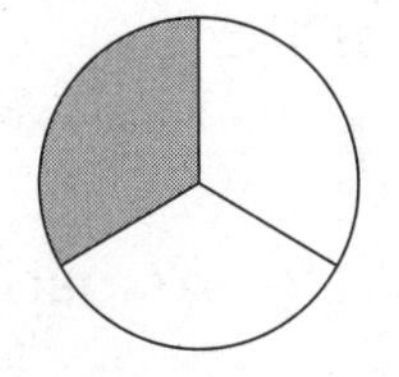

B. 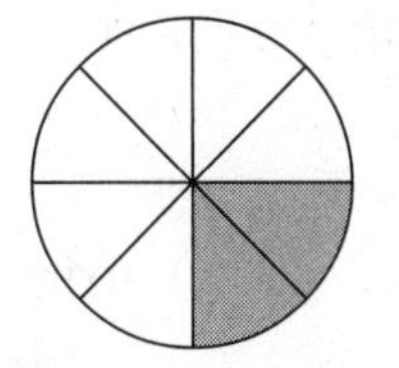

C. 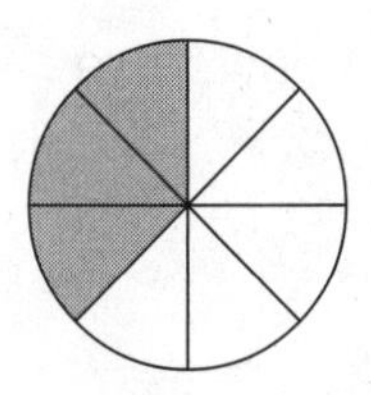

D. 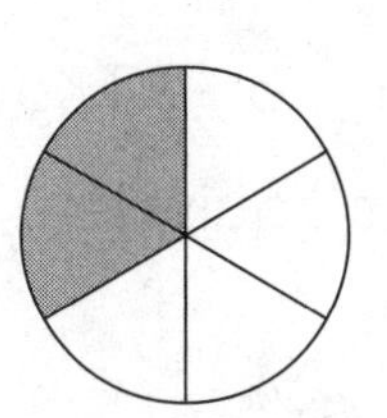

2. Look at the number line. Which fraction is equivalent to $\frac{6}{8}$?

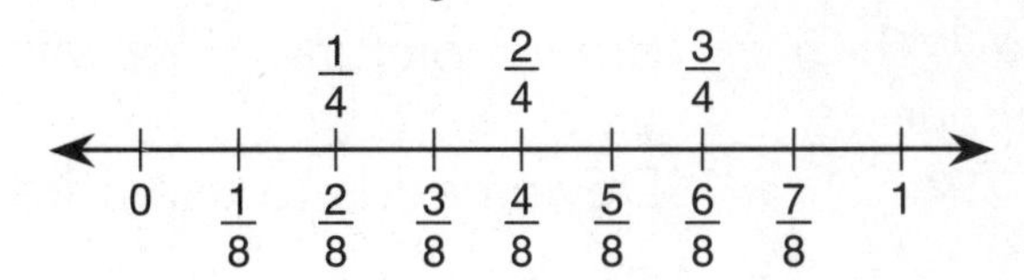

A. $\frac{1}{8}$

B. $\frac{1}{4}$

C. $\frac{2}{4}$

D. $\frac{3}{4}$

3. Elliot is making two banners. He wants the same fraction of each banner to be shaded. Shade the second banner to show how much Elliot should shade.

$\frac{2}{6}$

$\frac{1}{3}$

4. Eric planted $\frac{3}{6}$ of the garden with tomatoes and $\frac{1}{3}$ of the garden with cucumbers. Did he plant the same amount of the garden with tomatoes as with cucumbers? Explain.

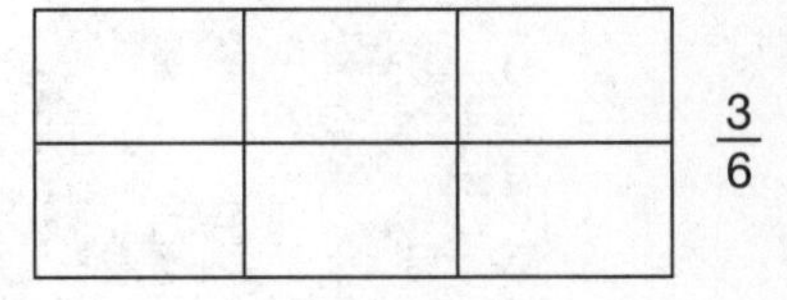

$\frac{3}{6}$

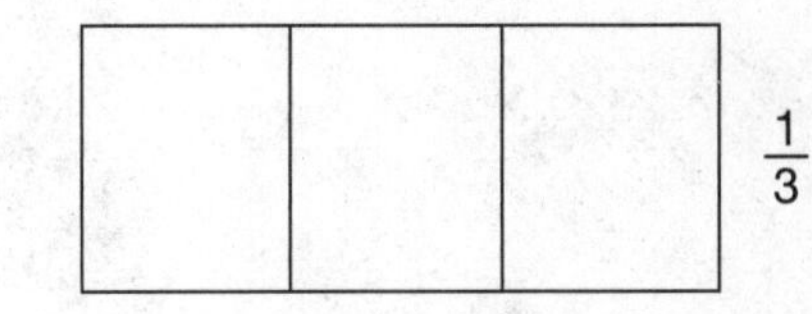

$\frac{1}{3}$

____

5. Look at the pattern. Complete the equivalent fractions. Can this pattern continue? How?

____

____

____

1								
$\frac{1}{3}$			$\frac{1}{3}$			$\frac{1}{3}$		
$\frac{1}{6}$	$\frac{1}{6}$		$\frac{1}{6}$	$\frac{1}{6}$		$\frac{1}{6}$	$\frac{1}{6}$	
$\frac{1}{9}$	$\frac{1}{9}$	$\frac{1}{9}$	$\frac{1}{9}$	$\frac{1}{9}$	$\frac{1}{9}$	$\frac{1}{9}$	$\frac{1}{9}$	$\frac{1}{9}$

Lesson 20 Generating Equivalent Fractions

3.NF.3.b Recognize and generate simple equivalent fractions, e.g., $\frac{1}{2} = \frac{2}{4}, \frac{4}{6} = \frac{2}{3}$. Explain why the fractions are equivalent, e.g., by using a visual fraction model.

Real World Connections

Key Word

equivalent fraction

Samantha has a sheet of paper divided into halves. Devin has a sheet of paper divided into fourths. They each will use $\frac{1}{2}$ of the paper to draw a picture. How will Devin know how much of his paper to use?

Devin needs to use a fraction of his paper that is equivalent to $\frac{1}{2}$. **Equivalent fractions** are fractions that name the same amount.

To find an equivalent fraction, find a fraction that names the same amount.

$\frac{1}{2}$ of Samantha's paper is shaded. The same amount of Devin's paper is shaded as Samantha's. But Devin's paper is divided into fourths. How many fourths are equivalent to $\frac{1}{2}$? Two of the four parts are shaded on Devin's paper, so $\frac{2}{4}$ is equivalent to $\frac{1}{2}$.

Model of Samantha's paper

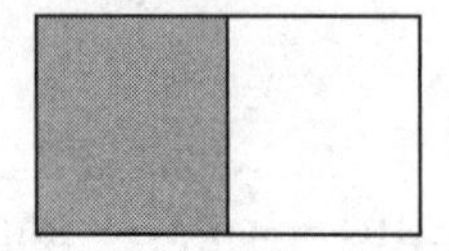

Model of Devin's paper

$$\frac{1}{2} = \frac{2}{4}$$

Take It Apart

Follow these steps to find equivalent fractions.

Step 1 Start with a fraction for which you want to find an equivalent fraction. You can use a fraction strip or a table to help you.

Find a fraction equivalent to $\frac{1}{4}$.

$\frac{1}{2}$					$\frac{1}{2}$						
$\frac{1}{3}$			$\frac{1}{3}$				$\frac{1}{3}$				
$\frac{1}{4}$		$\frac{1}{4}$			$\frac{1}{4}$			$\frac{1}{4}$			
$\frac{1}{6}$	$\frac{1}{6}$	$\frac{1}{6}$	$\frac{1}{6}$	$\frac{1}{6}$	$\frac{1}{6}$						
$\frac{1}{8}$	$\frac{1}{8}$	$\frac{1}{8}$	$\frac{1}{8}$	$\frac{1}{8}$	$\frac{1}{8}$	$\frac{1}{8}$	$\frac{1}{8}$				

Step 2 Think: What fraction names the same amount as $\frac{1}{4}$? Use the table to help you.

In the table, $\frac{1}{4}$ names the same amount as $\frac{2}{8}$.

$$\frac{1}{4} = \frac{2}{8}$$

Write the missing numerator. Use fraction strips to help you.

1.

$\frac{1}{2}$	$\frac{1}{2}$

$\frac{1}{8}$	$\frac{1}{8}$	$\frac{1}{8}$	$\frac{1}{8}$	$\frac{1}{8}$	$\frac{1}{8}$	$\frac{1}{8}$	$\frac{1}{8}$

$$\frac{1}{2} = \frac{}{8}$$

2.

$\frac{1}{6}$	$\frac{1}{6}$	$\frac{1}{6}$	$\frac{1}{6}$	$\frac{1}{6}$	$\frac{1}{6}$

$\frac{1}{3}$	$\frac{1}{3}$	$\frac{1}{3}$

$$\frac{4}{6} = \frac{}{3}$$

3.

$\frac{1}{4}$	$\frac{1}{4}$	$\frac{1}{4}$	$\frac{1}{4}$

$\frac{1}{8}$	$\frac{1}{8}$	$\frac{1}{8}$	$\frac{1}{8}$	$\frac{1}{8}$	$\frac{1}{8}$	$\frac{1}{8}$	$\frac{1}{8}$

$$\frac{3}{4} = \frac{}{8}$$

4.

$\frac{1}{2}$	$\frac{1}{2}$

$\frac{1}{4}$	$\frac{1}{4}$	$\frac{1}{4}$	$\frac{1}{4}$

$$\frac{1}{2} = \frac{}{4}$$

Put It Together

Write an equivalent fraction. Use the table if you need to.

1. $\frac{1}{2}$ = ____________
2. $\frac{3}{6}$ = ____________
3. $\frac{2}{4}$ = ____________
4. $\frac{2}{6}$ = ____________
5. $\frac{1}{4}$ = ____________
6. $\frac{4}{8}$ = ____________
7. $\frac{2}{8}$ = ____________
8. $\frac{2}{3}$ = ____________

<table>
<tr><td colspan="12">$\frac{1}{2}$</td><td colspan="12">$\frac{1}{2}$</td></tr>
<tr><td colspan="8">$\frac{1}{3}$</td><td colspan="8">$\frac{1}{3}$</td><td colspan="8">$\frac{1}{3}$</td></tr>
<tr><td colspan="6">$\frac{1}{4}$</td><td colspan="6">$\frac{1}{4}$</td><td colspan="6">$\frac{1}{4}$</td><td colspan="6">$\frac{1}{4}$</td></tr>
<tr><td colspan="4">$\frac{1}{6}$</td><td colspan="4">$\frac{1}{6}$</td><td colspan="4">$\frac{1}{6}$</td><td colspan="4">$\frac{1}{6}$</td><td colspan="4">$\frac{1}{6}$</td><td colspan="4">$\frac{1}{6}$</td></tr>
<tr><td colspan="3">$\frac{1}{8}$</td><td colspan="3">$\frac{1}{8}$</td><td colspan="3">$\frac{1}{8}$</td><td colspan="3">$\frac{1}{8}$</td><td colspan="3">$\frac{1}{8}$</td><td colspan="3">$\frac{1}{8}$</td><td colspan="3">$\frac{1}{8}$</td><td colspan="3">$\frac{1}{8}$</td></tr>
</table>

Write an equivalent fraction. Draw a model to show the two fractions are equivalent.

9. $\frac{4}{6}$ = ____________
10. $\frac{3}{4}$ = ____________

Answer the questions. Share your ideas with a classmate.

11. Can you find an equivalent fraction for $\frac{1}{4}$ that has 6 as its denominator? Explain.

____

____

12. Tim is making a quilt. He made $\frac{1}{4}$ of the quilt red. Use the model to find a fraction that is equivalent to $\frac{1}{4}$. Explain how you changed the model.

____

____

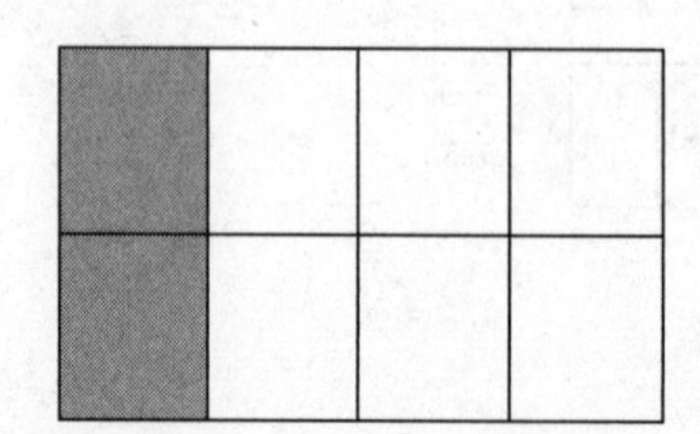

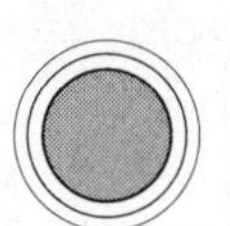

Make It Work

Answer the questions below.

1. The bar shows $\frac{3}{4}$ shaded. Which fraction is equivalent to $\frac{3}{4}$?

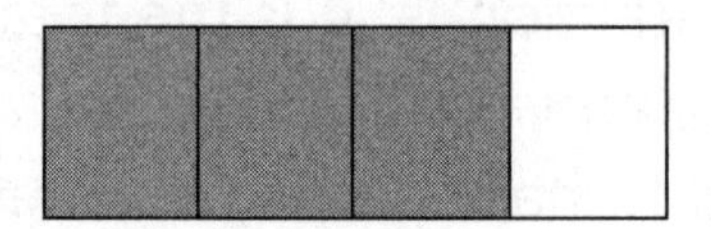

A. $\frac{1}{2}$

B. $\frac{2}{3}$

C. $\frac{6}{8}$

D. $\frac{5}{6}$

2. The picture below shows equivalent fractions. Which fraction is not equivalent?

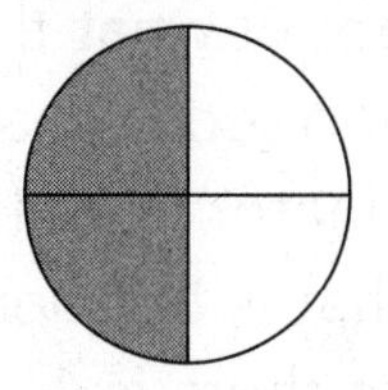

A. $\frac{2}{4}$ **B.** $\frac{3}{6}$

C. $\frac{1}{2}$ **D.** $\frac{5}{8}$

3. Use the picture to write two equivalent fractions.

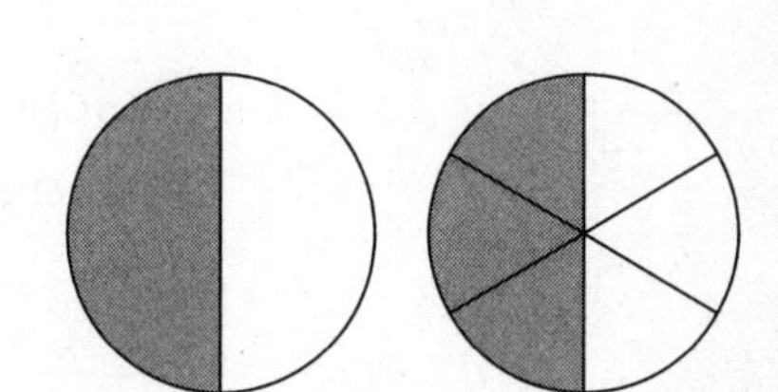

____

4. The bar shows $\frac{3}{6}$ shaded. Use the bar to write an equivalent fraction for $\frac{3}{6}$. Draw a model to show the two fractions are equivalent.

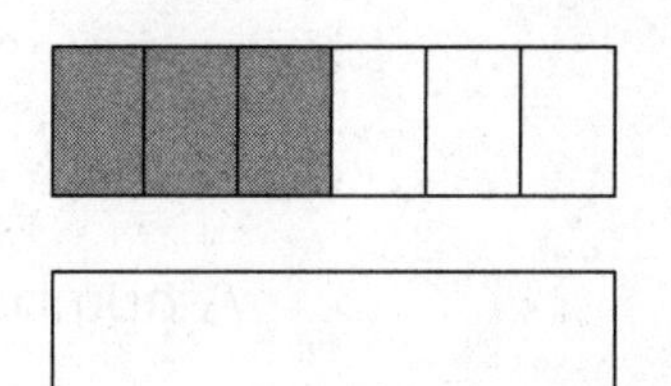

____

5. Use the table. Complete the equivalent fractions. What pattern do you see?

____

____

____

1							
$\frac{1}{2}$				$\frac{1}{2}$			

Lesson 21 Expressing Whole Numbers as Fractions

3.NF.3.c Express whole numbers as fractions, and recognize fractions that are equivalent to whole numbers. *Examples: Express 3 in the form* $3 = \frac{3}{1}$*; recognize that* $\frac{6}{1} = 6$*; locate* $\frac{4}{4}$ *and 1 at the same point of a number line diagram.*

Real World Connections

Key Words

fraction

Alina has 4 whole apples. How can she write the number of apples she has as a fraction? Remember, a **fraction** names part of a whole.

Think about what the denominator of a fraction is. It is the total number of equal parts. If a whole is divided into fourths, the denominator is 4. If a whole is divided into halves, the denominator is 2. What is the denominator if the whole is not divided? It is 1, because there is 1 equal part.

$\frac{4}{1}$ number of parts considered / total number of equal parts

$\frac{4}{1} = 4$

A fraction is equivalent to 1 if the numerator and the denominator are the same number.

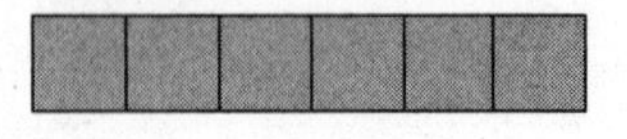

$\frac{6}{6}$ number of parts considered / total number of equal parts

$\frac{6}{6} = 1$

A number line can help you see that a fraction can be equivalent to 1.

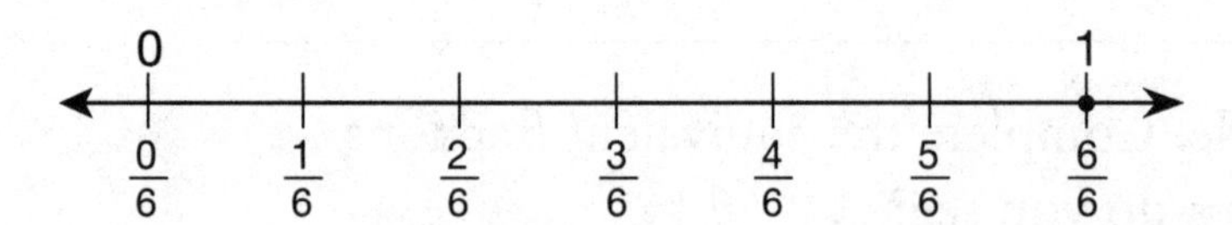

Take It Apart

To write a whole number as a fraction, write the whole number as the numerator and 1 as the denominator.

$5 = \frac{5}{1}$ $\qquad$ $8 = \frac{8}{1}$ $\qquad$ $50 = \frac{50}{1}$

To write a fraction equivalent to 1, follow these steps.

Step 1 Count the total number of equal parts. This is the denominator.

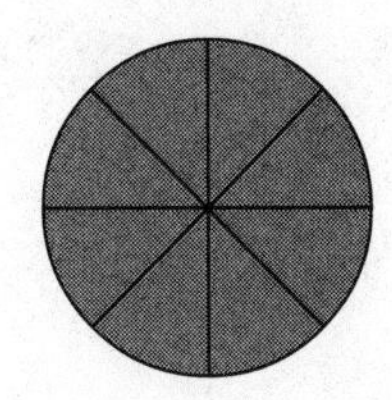

There are 8 equal parts.

Step 2 Write the same number for the numerator as you did for the denominator.

$\frac{8}{8} = 1$

Write each whole number as a fraction. Use the models to help you.

1.

$\frac{\quad}{1}$

2.  

$\frac{\quad}{1}$

3. Use the number line. What fraction is equal to 1?

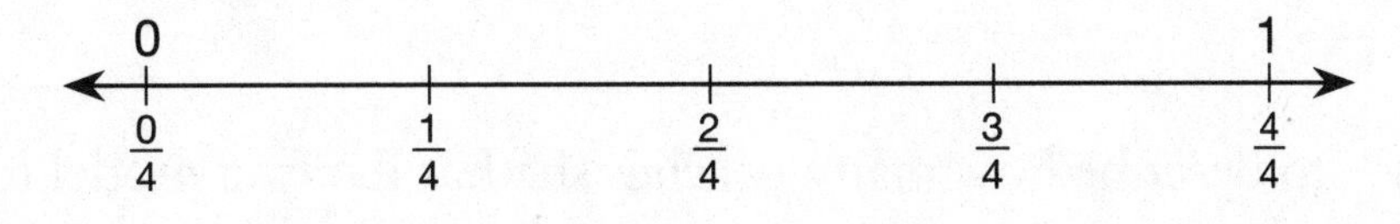

____

Put It Together

Write each whole number as a fraction.

1.  ______

2. 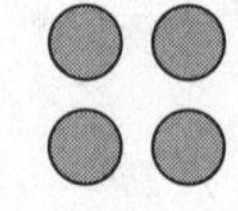 ______

3. 2 ______ **4.** 3 ______ **5.** 8 ______

Write each fraction as a whole number.

6. $\frac{4}{1}$ ______ **7.** $\frac{8}{1}$ ______ **8.** $\frac{5}{5}$ ______

9. $\frac{5}{1}$ ______ **10.** $\frac{6}{6}$ ______ **11.** $\frac{3}{1}$ ______

Write the fraction that is equal to 1 on each number line.

12. 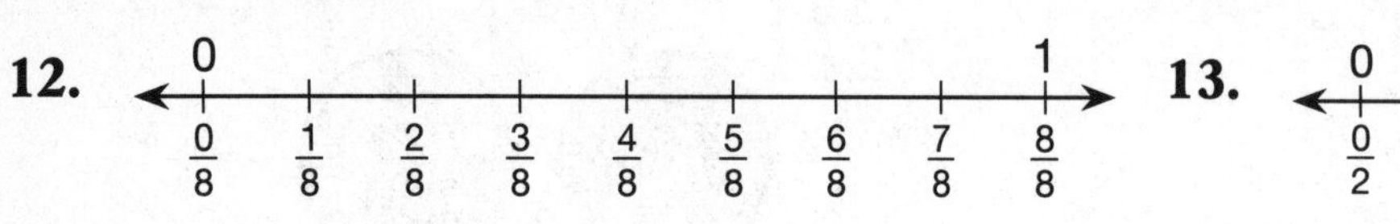

______

13. 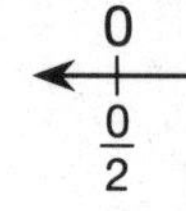 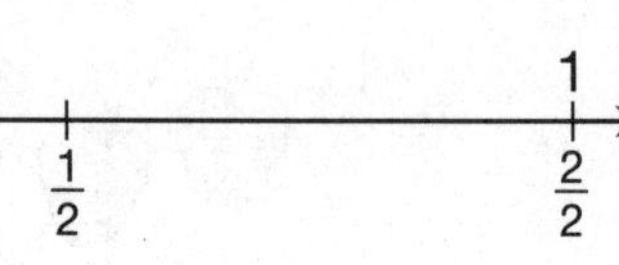

______

Answer the questions. Share your ideas with a classmate.

14. How can you know just by looking at a fraction that it is equal to 1?

____

15. Kate wrote the fraction $\frac{5}{1}$ to describe how many peaches she has. Draw a model to show how many peaches she has. Explain how she can write this as a fraction.

____

____

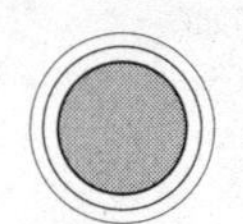

Make It Work

Answer the questions below.

1. Which shows the number of buttons written as a fraction?

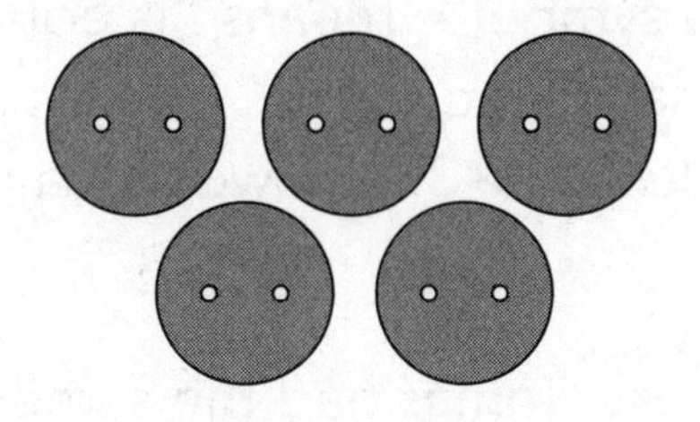

A. $\frac{1}{5}$

B. $\frac{2}{5}$

C. $\frac{5}{5}$

D. $\frac{5}{1}$

2. Which whole number is equivalent to $\frac{8}{8}$?

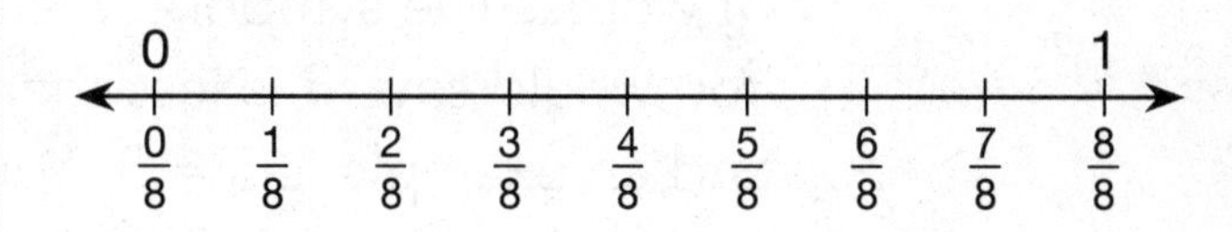

A. 0

B. 1

C. 2

D. 3

3. Andrew has 6 pinecones. Write the number of pinecones he has as a fraction.

____

4. Elizabeth ate $\frac{4}{4}$ of her sandwich. How much of her sandwich did she eat? Explain.

____

5. Veronica wrote $\frac{3}{4} = 1$. Draw a number line to explain her mistake.

____

____

____

____

Lesson 22 Comparing Fractions

3.NF.3.d Compare two fractions with the same numerator or the same denominator by reasoning about their size. Recognize that comparisons are valid only when the two fractions refer to the same whole. Record the results of comparisons with the symbols >, =, or <, and justify the conclusions, e.g., by using a visual fraction model.

Real World Connections

Keep in mind that when you compare, you can use symbols instead of words. The symbol < means "less than" and an example is 3 < 5. You would say "3 is less than 5." The symbol = means "is equal to" and an example is 5 = 5. You would say "5 equals 5." The symbol > means "greater than" and an example is 5 > 3. You would say "5 is greater than 3."

Emma finished $\frac{1}{4}$ of her math homework. Tomas had the same math homework. He finished $\frac{1}{3}$ of his math homework. How can you find out who finished more?

You can compare fractions similarly to how you compare whole numbers. You can only compare fractions that refer to the same whole. You cannot compare $\frac{1}{3}$ of a sandwich and $\frac{1}{4}$ of a juice box, but you can compare $\frac{1}{3}$ and $\frac{1}{4}$ of the same sandwich.

Compare fractions with the same numerator.

If the numerators are the same, the fraction with the larger denominator is smaller. A larger denominator means the whole is divided into more parts, so each part is smaller.

Compare fractions with the same denominator.

If the denominators are the same, the fraction with the larger numerator is greater. A larger numerator means there are more of the same equal parts.

Take It Apart

Follow these steps to compare fractions with the same numerator or same denominator.

Step 1 Look at the numerators and denominators of the two fractions. Are the numerators or denominators the same?

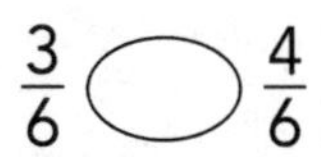

$\frac{3}{6} \bigcirc \frac{4}{6}$ $\qquad$ $\frac{2}{6} \bigcirc \frac{2}{8}$

same denominator $\qquad$ same numerator

Step 2 If the denominators are the same, compare the numerators. The fraction with the largest numerator is greater.

$\frac{3}{6} \bigcirc \frac{4}{6}$ $\qquad$ $3 < 4$ so $\frac{3}{6} < \frac{4}{6}$

same denominator

Step 3 If the numerators are the same, compare the denominators. The fraction with the largest denominator is the smaller fraction.

$\frac{2}{6} \bigcirc \frac{2}{8}$ $\qquad$ $6 < 8$ so $\frac{2}{6} > \frac{2}{8}$

same numerator

Use the models to compare. Write >, <, or =.

1.

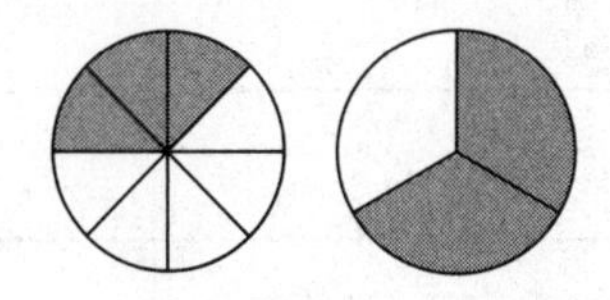

$\frac{3}{8} \bigcirc \frac{2}{3}$

2.

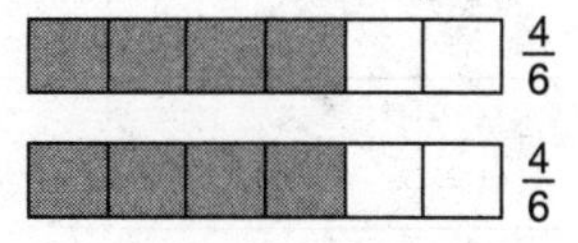

$\frac{4}{6} \bigcirc \frac{4}{6}$

3.

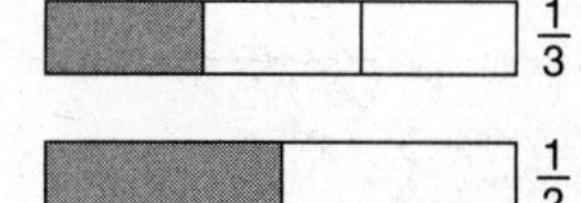

$\frac{1}{3} \bigcirc \frac{1}{2}$

Put It Together

Use the symbols >, <, or = to compare the fractions.

1. $\frac{1}{6}$ ◯ $\frac{1}{8}$
2. $\frac{2}{3}$ ◯ $\frac{2}{4}$
3. $\frac{4}{6}$ ◯ $\frac{4}{4}$
4. $\frac{5}{8}$ ◯ $\frac{5}{6}$
5. $\frac{1}{3}$ ◯ $\frac{2}{3}$
6. $\frac{2}{4}$ ◯ $\frac{2}{8}$
7. $\frac{3}{4}$ ◯ $\frac{3}{4}$
8. $\frac{2}{8}$ ◯ $\frac{5}{8}$
9. $\frac{1}{4}$ ◯ $\frac{1}{2}$
10. $\frac{5}{8}$ ◯ $\frac{2}{8}$
11. $\frac{2}{4}$ ◯ $\frac{2}{3}$
12. $\frac{2}{3}$ ◯ $\frac{2}{8}$

Answer the questions. Share your ideas with a classmate.

13. Lora divides a pizza into slices. Will the slices be larger if she divides the pizza into 6 slices or 8 slices? Draw models to explain.

____

____

14. A muffin recipe calls for $\frac{3}{4}$ cup of flour, $\frac{1}{4}$ cup of cocoa, and $\frac{2}{4}$ cup of sugar. Which ingredient is used in the greatest amount? Explain how you found the answer.

____

____

____

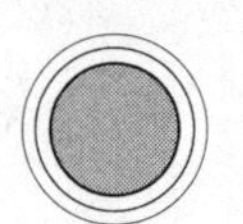

Make It Work

Answer the questions below.

1. The model shows $\frac{3}{8}$ shaded.

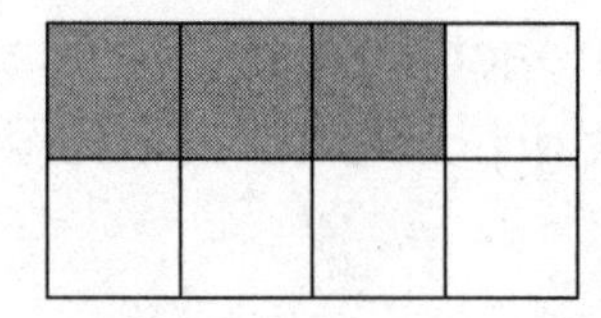

Which fraction is more than the shaded part?

A. $\frac{1}{8}$ **C.** $\frac{3}{8}$

B. $\frac{2}{8}$ **D.** $\frac{4}{8}$

2. Which number sentence is correct?

A. $\frac{3}{8} < \frac{3}{6}$

B. $\frac{3}{6} > \frac{4}{6}$

C. $\frac{3}{8} > \frac{3}{6}$

D. $\frac{3}{6} = \frac{4}{6}$

3. Miranda ran $\frac{1}{4}$ of a mile. Alejandro ran $\frac{1}{8}$ of a mile. Who ran farther? Draw a model to explain.

____

____

4. Jamie read $\frac{3}{4}$ of the reading assignment. Adam read less of the reading assignment than Jamie. Write a fraction that could be the amount that Adam read. Explain how you know the fraction is smaller.

____

____

5. Alison spends $\frac{4}{6}$ of an hour doing her homework. Does she spend most of the hour doing her homework? Explain how you decided.

____

____

____

____

Chapter 3

Question 1: How can paper help you understand fractions?

You can divide a piece of paper into fractions just by folding it. Take a sheet of paper. Fold it in half. How many parts do you have? You have two. Now write the fraction of the paper on each half of the paper. If there are two equal parts and you are writing on one of the parts, the fraction is $\frac{1}{2}$.

Now fold the paper in half again. When you open it, how many equal parts do you have now? Four. Label each fourth of the paper $\frac{1}{4}$. Keep going. Fold the paper in half again. Now you're up to eighths. Label each eighth. How far can you go? How tiny can you fold your paper? Keep folding and labeling fractions until you can't fold your paper anymore. Challenge your classmates to see who can fold his or her paper into the smallest fraction.

Question 2: How many fractions can you fit on a number line?

You can show fractions on a number line from 0 to 1. You can divide the distance from 0 to 1 in many different ways. Make a poster-size number line from 0 to 1 with a partner. Begin by dividing the number line in half and labeling $\frac{1}{2}$. Then divide it into thirds and label $\frac{1}{3}$, $\frac{2}{3}$, and $\frac{3}{3}$. Use a different color for each set of fractions. For example, write the halves in blue and the thirds in red. Then divide it into fourths and label $\frac{1}{4}$, $\frac{2}{4}$, $\frac{3}{4}$, and $\frac{4}{4}$. Continue dividing the number line into sixths and then eighths.

Once your number line is complete, write 5 questions for your partner to answer about fractions on a number line, equivalent fractions, or comparing fractions. Trade your questions with your partner and answer your partner's questions.

Question 3: How do you know two fractions are equivalent?

Equivalent fractions name the same amount. If you colored $\frac{1}{2}$ of a picture, you also colored $\frac{2}{4}$ of it, or $\frac{4}{8}$ of it. Circle models can help you understand equivalent fractions.

You will need 6 circles that are the same size. Divide one circle into halves, one into thirds, one into fourths, one into sixths, and one into eighths. Leave the last circle whole. Then cut $\frac{1}{2}$ out of the circle divided into halves. Cut out $\frac{1}{3}$ of the circle divided into thirds, $\frac{1}{4}$ out of the one divided into fourths, and so on.

Now you can use your circles to find equivalent fractions. Do you want to know how many eighths are equivalent to $\frac{1}{2}$? Line up the middle of the halves circle on top of the eighths circle. How many eighths are showing? Use your circles to write at least 8 equivalent fractions. Then use the whole circle to help you write a fraction that is equivalent to 1 for each of the circles.

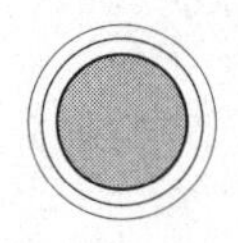

Question 4: What happens when you switch the numerator and the denominator of a fraction?

The numerator and the denominator of a fraction have important jobs. The denominator tells how many equal parts a whole is divided into. The numerator tells how many of those parts are being considered. If $\frac{1}{3}$ of a circle is shaded, it means the circle is divided into 3 equal parts and 1 of those parts is shaded.

You can see the important roles of the numerator and denominator when you switch them. Think about $\frac{1}{3}$ and $\frac{3}{1}$. How are they different? $\frac{1}{3}$ represents 1 part of 3 equal parts of a whole. $\frac{3}{1}$ represents 3 equal wholes.

Write several fractions that have 1 as the numerator. Make a model for each fraction. Then flip the fractions upside-down. Now make a model for that fraction. You will make 2 models for each fraction you write. Mix all of the fractions and models up. Trade your fractions and models with a partner. Then group your partner's fractions and models together and show your partner which model goes with the fraction when it is right-side-up and which model goes with the fraction when it is upside-down.

Solving Problems Involving Time

3.MD.1 Tell and write time to the nearest minute and measure time intervals in minutes. Solve word problems involving addition and subtraction of time intervals in minutes, e.g., by representing the problem on a number line diagram.

Real World Connections

Toolbox

clocks with moveable hands

number lines

Key Words

minute

hour

elapsed time

You use time throughout the day. You use time to know when you need to be at school, how long lunch lasts, and what time you go to bed.

The clock shows the time Ling gets on the school bus each afternoon. What time does Ling get on the school bus?

The hands, numbers, and marks on a clock tell you what time it is. In 5 minutes, the minute hand moves from one number to the next. In 1 **minute**, the minute hand moves from one mark to the next.

To find the time, first find where the hour hand is. It is between 2 and 3, so the **hour** is 2.

To find the number of minutes after the hour, count by fives and ones to where the minute hand is pointing.

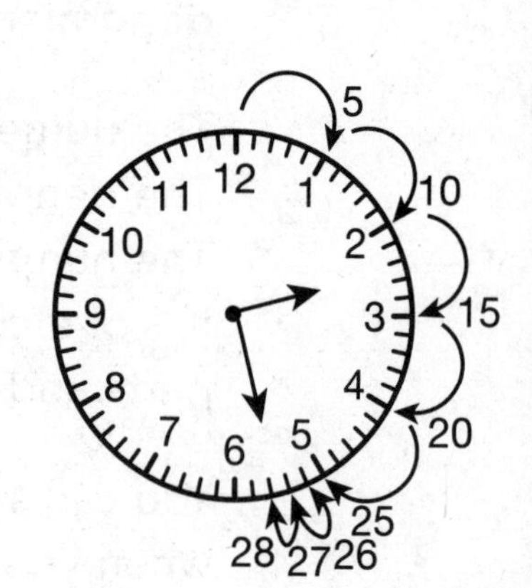

The time is 28 minutes after the hour.

Read the time by saying: two twenty-eight or twenty-eight minutes after two.

Write the time as: 2:28.

Ling gets on the school bus at 2:28.

Take It Apart

Soccer practice starts at 10:15 A.M. It ends at 11:00 A.M. How long is soccer practice?

To find the amount of time that passes from the start of an activity to the end of an activity, or **elapsed time,** you can follow either of these methods.

Method 1 Use a clock with moveable hands.

Step 1 Show the start time.

Method 2 Use a number line.

Step 1 Find the start time and end time.

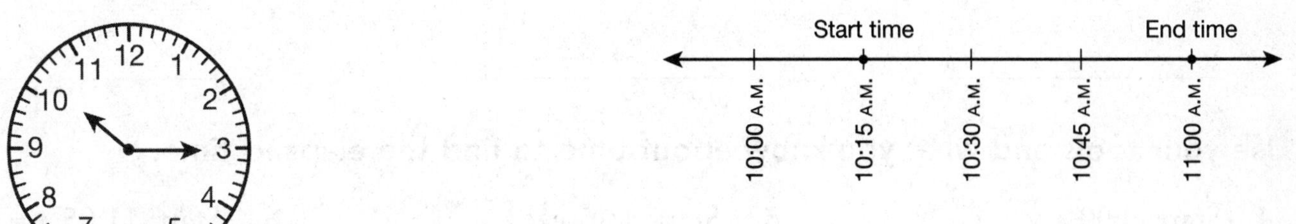

Step 2 Count the minutes to the end time.

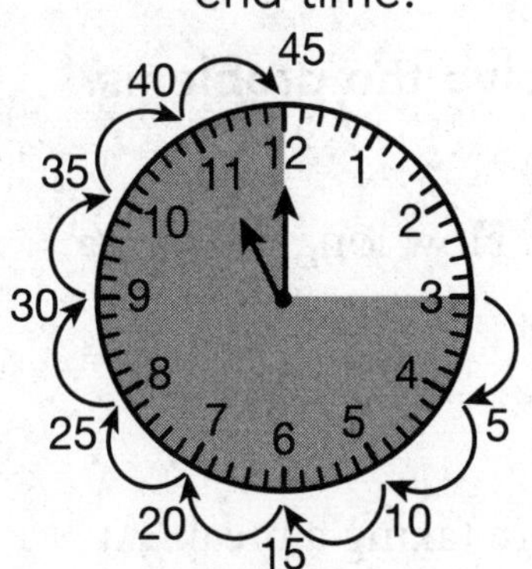

Soccer practice is 45 minutes long.

Step 2 Count the minutes to the end time.

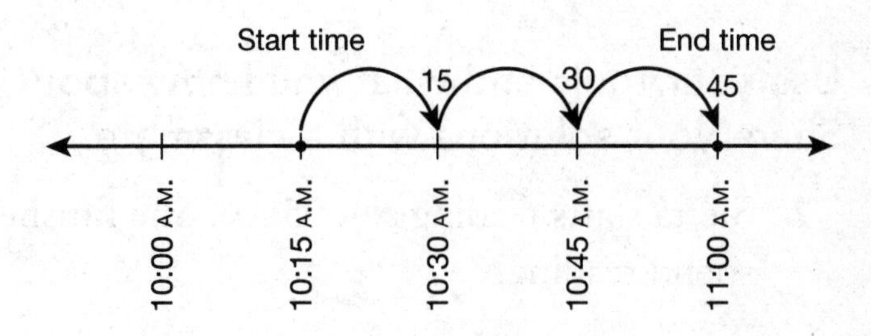

Soccer practice is 45 minutes long.

Use your tools and what you know about elapsed time to solve the problems.

1. Juan arrives to the movie theater at 4:35 P.M. He waits 15 minutes for his sister to join him. What time does Juan's sister arrive at the movie theater?

____

2. A concert starts at 8:05 P.M. and ends at 8:55 P.M. How long was the concert?

____

3. Sarah starting painting at 10:20 A.M. and finished at 10:51 A.M. For how long did Sarah paint?

____

Put It Together

Write the time shown on each clock.

1. 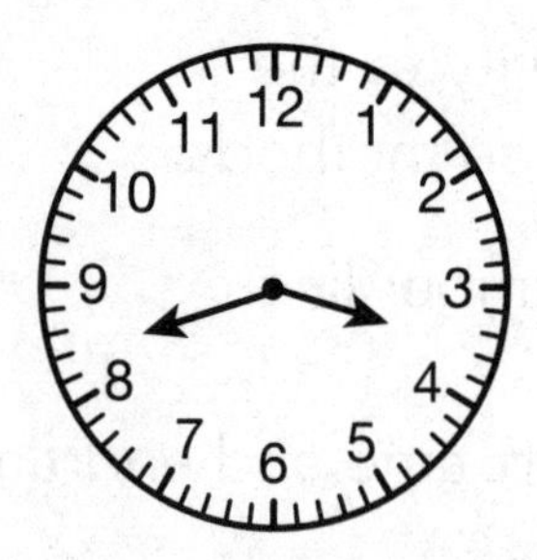

____

2. 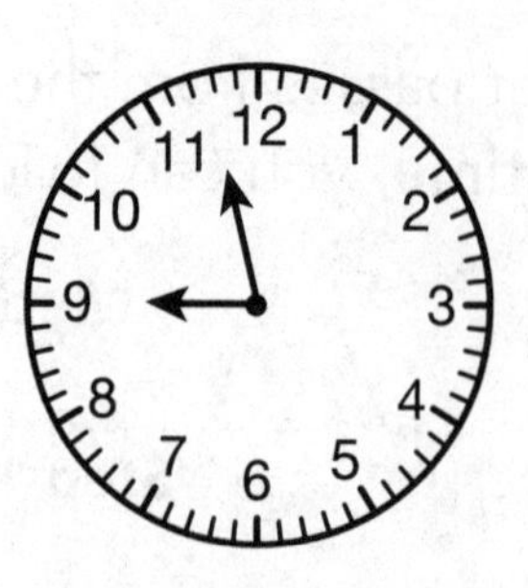

____

3. 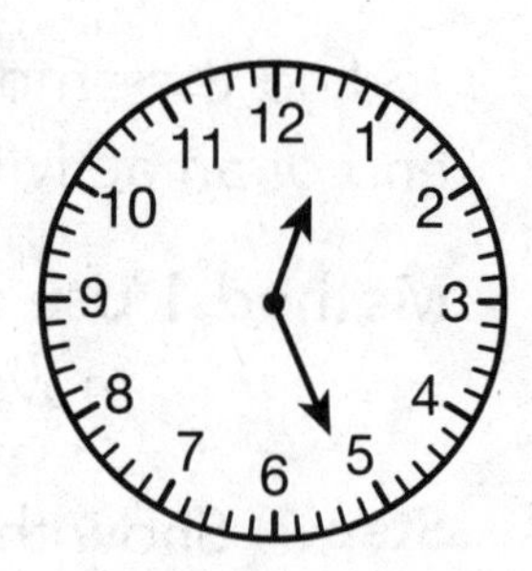

____

Use your tools and what you know about time to find the elapsed time.

4. Start: 9:00 A.M.
End: 9:35 A.M.

____

5. Start: 1:15 P.M.
End: 1:52 P.M.

____

6. Start: 11:05 A.M.
End: 11:21 A.M.

____

Use your tools and what you know about elapsed time to solve the problems. Share your solutions with a classmate.

7. Sierra starts reading at 4:05 P.M. She finishes reading at 4:43 P.M. How long did Sierra spend reading?

____

8. Bob starts swimming at 7:25 P.M. He swims for 26 minutes before taking a break. At what time does Bob stop swimming to take a break?

____

9. Kara starts her spelling homework at 3:18 P.M. She finishes her spelling homework at 3:36 P.M. How long did Kara's spelling homework take?

____

10. A student knows the elapsed time and the end time of an activity. How can the student find the start time of the activity?

____

____

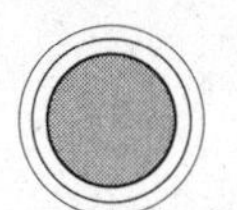

Make It Work

Answer the questions below.

1. What time is shown on the clock?

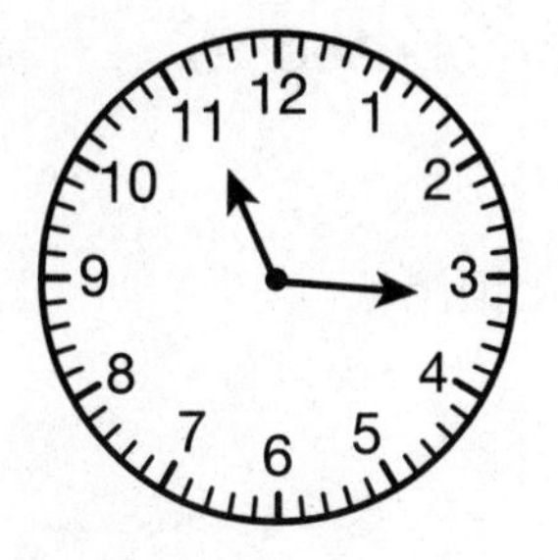

A. 10:16 **B.** 11:31

C. 11:16 **D.** 3:57

2. A football game is supposed to start at 4:30 P.M. It starts 23 minutes late. What time does the football game begin?

A. 4:23 P.M.

B. 4:43 P.M.

C. 4:48 P.M.

D. 4:53 P.M.

3. Cam played a video game from 8:15 P.M. to 8:43 P.M. How long did Cam play the video game?

____

4. Lavina takes her dog for a 25-minute walk. She leaves her house at 4:19 P.M. What time does Lavina get home from the walk?

____

5. Think about two activities you do on a school day and how much time each takes. Write two time problems about your activities where start time, end time, or elapsed time needs to be calculated. Then solve the problems.

____

____

____

Measuring and Estimating Liquid Volume

3.MD.2 Measure and estimate liquid volumes and masses of objects using standard units of grams (g), kilograms (kg), and liters (l). Add, subtract, multiply, or divide to solve one-step word problems involving masses or volumes that are given in the same units, e.g., by using drawings (such as a beaker with a measurement scale) to represent the problem.

Real World Connections

Key Words

- volume
- milliliter (mL)
- liter (L)

The capacity, or **volume**, of a container is the amount a container can hold. **Milliliter (mL)** and **liter (L)** are two metric units used to measure volume.

You can use common objects to help you estimate volume.

There are 1,000 milliliters in 1 liter.

Which is the best estimate of the volume of this bucket, 10 mL, 10 L, or 100 L?

Think: The bucket is large, so use a large unit of volume. Estimate the volume in liters.

10 L is about the volume of 10 water bottles, that is a more reasonable estimate than 100 L.

The best estimate of the bucket's volume is 10 L.

Take It Apart

Coach Simon has 8 liters of sports drink. He gives an equal amount to 4 players. How many liters of sports drink does each player get?

To solve the problem, you can use either of these methods.

Method 1 Draw a picture.

Step 1 Show the total volume.

Step 2 Circle 4 groups of 2.

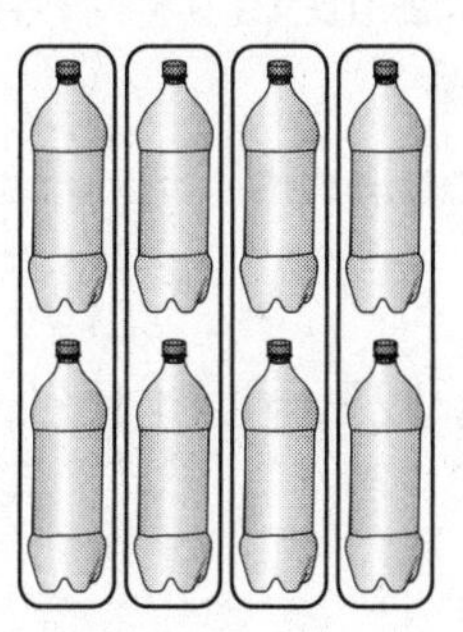

Each player gets 2 liters of sports drink.

Method 2 Write a number sentence.

Step 1 Decide what operation to use. A number is equally shared, so use division.

Step 2 Write and solve the number sentence.
8 liters ÷ 4 players = 2 liters

Each player gets 2 liters of sports drink.

Use what you know about volume to solve the problems.

1. Mrs. Chang is having a party. She has eight 2-liter bottles of juice. How many liters of juice does she have in all?

____

2. Cora fills a saucepan with water. Which is the better estimate of how much water Cora puts in the saucepan, 8 mL or 8 L? Explain your reasoning.

____

____

Put It Together

Circle the better estimate for the volume of each object.

1. 

1 mL or 1 L

2. 

3 liters or 30 liters

3. 

40 mL or 400 mL

4. 

3 L or 30 L

5. 

2 milliliters or 2 liters

6. 

40 L or 400 L

Use what you know about volume to solve the problems. Share your solutions with a classmate.

7. Carolina has 900 mL of water in a bottle. She drinks 125 mL of the water. How much water is left in the bottle?

____

8. Mr. Roberts buys three packs of 1-liter water bottles. Each pack has 15 water bottles. How many liters of water does Mr. Roberts buy in all?

____

9. A student estimates the volume of an object is 10 mL. What type of object could the student be looking at? Explain your reasoning.

____

____

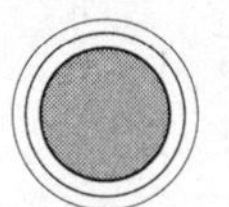

Make It Work

Answer the questions below.

1. Which is the best estimate of the pool's volume?

A. 4 mL **B.** 40 L

C. 40 mL **D.** 400 L

2. The snack shop buys cases of water. Each case has 24 liters of water in it. How many liters of water are in 3 cases?

A. 72 liters **B.** 27 liters

C. 62 liters **D.** 8 liters

3. Kwan needs 1,000 mL of water for a science project. He has measured 325 mL so far. How much more water does Kwan need?

____

4. Lucy estimates that the volume of a drinking cup is 20 liters. Is this estimate reasonable? Explain why or why not.

____

____

5. Suppose you compare two empty containers that are different sizes. Could you estimate which container has the greater volume only by looking at it? Explain.

____

____

____

Measuring and Estimating Mass

3.MD.2 Measure and estimate liquid volumes and masses of objects using standard units of grams (g), kilograms (kg), and liters (l). Add, subtract, multiply, or divide to solve one-step word problems involving masses or volumes that are given in the same units, e.g., by using drawings (such as a beaker with a measurement scale) to represent the problem.

Real World Connections

Key Words

- mass
- gram (g)
- kilogram (kg)

The **mass** tells how much matter is in something. The **gram (g)** and **kilogram (kg)** are two metric units used to measure mass.

You can use common objects to help you estimate mass.

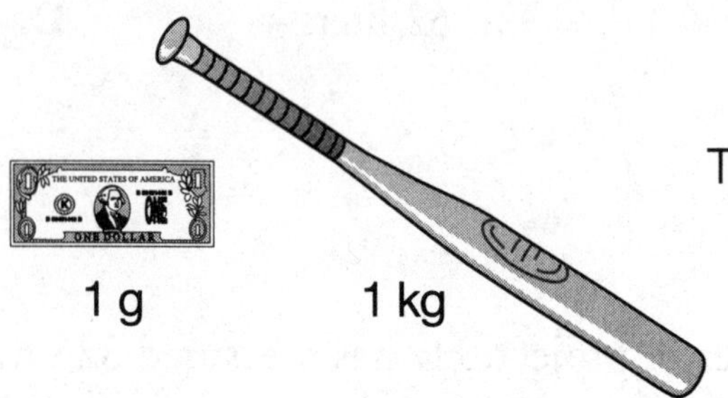

There are 1,000 grams in 1 kilogram.

Which is the best estimate of the mass of this marker, 10 grams, 100 grams, or 10 kilograms?

Think: The marker does not have a lot of mass, so use a small unit of mass. Estimate the mass in grams.

10 grams is about the mass of 10 dollar bills. That is a more reasonable estimate than 100 grams.

The best estimate of the marker's mass is 10 grams.

Take It Apart

A fruit supplier is shipping out a box of watermelons. Each watermelon has a mass of about 3 kilograms and there are 9 watermelons in the box. What is the best estimate for the mass of the box?

To solve the problem, you can use either of these methods.

Method 1 Draw a picture.

Step 1 Show the mass of each watermelon.

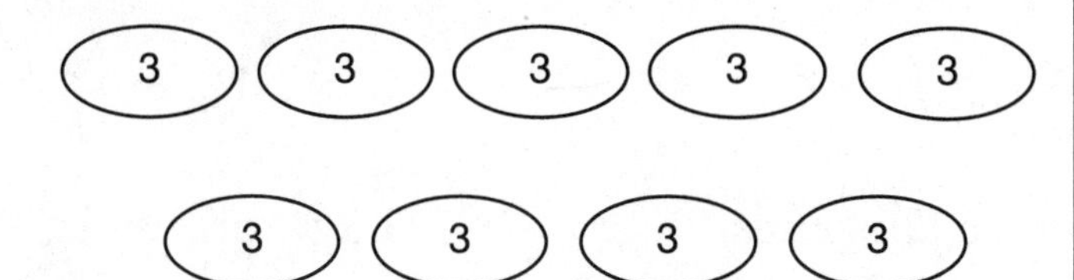

Step 2 Skip count to find the total mass.

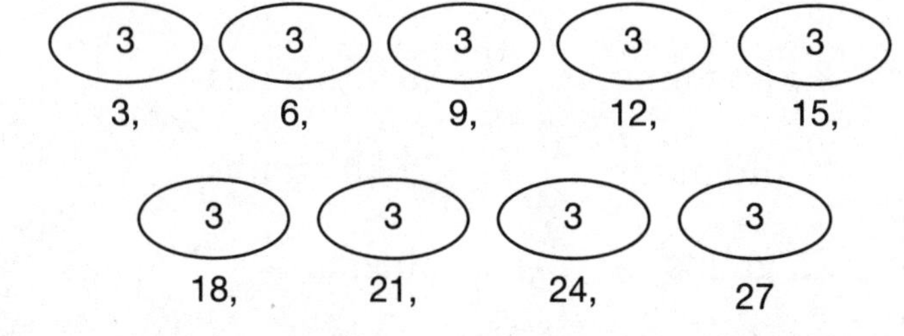

The box has a mass of about 27 kilograms.

Method 2 Write a number sentence.

Step 1 Decide what operation to use. You can use multiplication.

Step 2 Write and solve the number sentence. 3 kilograms × 9 watermelons = 27 kilograms

The box has a mass of about 27 kilograms

Use what you know about mass to solve the problems.

1. A laptop has a mass of 2 kilograms. A shipment of laptops has a mass of 24 kilograms. How many laptops are in the shipment?

____

2. An apple has a mass of 700 grams. Carmen cores the apple and finds that the mass of the core is 125 grams. What is the mass of the remaining apple?

____

3. Alfredo has 5 strawberries for a snack. Which is the better estimate for the mass of the strawberries, 15 grams or 15 kilograms? Explain your reasoning.

____

____

Put It Together

Circle the better estimate for the mass of each object.

1. 

1 g or 1 kg

2. 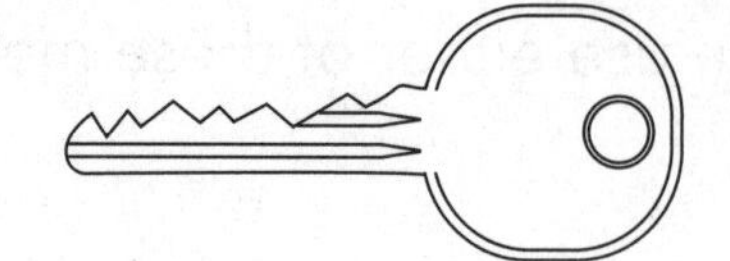

6 grams or 6 kilograms

3. 

1 kg or 10 kg

Circle the best estimate for the mass of each object.

4. a sneaker	800 grams	8 kilograms	80 kilograms
5. a cat	5 grams	5 kilograms	25 kilograms
6. a paper clip	1 gram	25 grams	50 grams

Use what you know about mass to solve the problems. Share your solutions with a classmate.

7. A marble has a mass of 45 grams. Sam has 2 marbles. What is the total mass of Sam's marbles?

____

8. A large box of blocks has a mass of 60 kilograms. Each block has a mass of 4 kilograms. How many blocks are in the box?

____

9. A nickel has a mass of about 5 grams. What is another object that has a mass of about 5 grams?

____

____

Make It Work

Answer the questions below.

1. Which is the best estimate of the mass of a spider?

A. 2 grams

B. 200 grams

C. 2 kilograms

D. 200 kilograms

2. A book has a mass of 2 kilograms. Mrs. Wilson is carrying a stack of 6 books. What is the mass of all the books she is carrying?

A. 3 kilograms

B. 8 kilograms

C. 12 kilograms

D. 22 kilograms

3. A 2 month old puppy has a mass of 5 kilograms. By the time it is an adult its mass will be 4 times greater. What will the mass of the adult dog be?

____

4. A student finds the mass of a grape and records the answer as 4 grams. Is this mass reasonable? Explain.

____

____

5. Do objects of about the same size always have about the same mass? Explain your reasoning.

____

____

____

Lesson 26 Drawing and Interpreting Scaled Picture Graphs

3.MD.3 Draw a scaled picture graph and a scaled bar graph to represent a data set with several categories. Solve one- and two-step "how many more" and "how many less" problems using information presented in scaled bar graphs. *For example, draw a bar graph in which each square in the bar graph might represent 5 pets.*

Real World Connections

Key Words

picture graph

key

A **picture graph** shows data using symbols, or pictures. You may see picture graphs in your science or social studies books, in newspapers, or in other books you read. Graphs are a useful way to show data because they allow you to compare the data quickly.

Carmen surveyed her classmates and asked them to name their favorite pet. Twelve students chose dog, 11 students chose cat, and 7 students chose hamster. She made a picture graph of the data.

Favorite Pets

Dog	🐾 🐾 🐾 🐾 🐾 🐾
Cat	🐾 🐾 🐾 🐾 🐾 ½🐾
Hamster	🐾 🐾 🐾 ½🐾

Key: 🐾 = 2 students

Look at the **key**. It shows you that every 🐾 stands for 2 students.

This means that to count the number of students who voted for dog, you skip count by 2s. There are 6 🐾, so count: 2, 4, 6, 8, 10, 12. There were 12 students who voted for dog.

Look in the row for cat. The last symbol is cut in half, ½🐾. This means that symbol stands for half the number of a whole symbol. In this case, half a paw print stands for 1 student.

To find the number of students who voted for cat, first skip count the number of whole paw prints: 2, 4, 6, 8, 10. Then count on 1 for the half paw print: 11. There were 11 students who voted for cat.

To find the number of students who voted for hamster, first skip count the number of whole paw prints: 2, 4, 6. Then count on 1 for the half paw print: 7. There were 7 students who voted for hamster.

Take It Apart

Follow the steps to make a picture graph of the tally chart.

James counts the number of each kind of tree he sees in the park. He records his data in the tally table shown.

Trees in the Park

Kind of Tree	Number of Trees
Elm	𝍸 𝍸 𝍸 𝍸 𝍸 𝍸 𝍸 𝍸
Maple	𝍸 𝍸 𝍸
Oak	𝍸 𝍸 𝍸 𝍸 𝍸
Pine	𝍸 𝍸 𝍸 𝍸 𝍸 𝍸 𝍸 𝍸 𝍸 𝍸

Step 1 Choose a title that tells about the graph. Trees in the Park is a good choice because it tells what the graph is about.

Step 2 Choose a symbol to represent the data. A 🌳 is a good choice because the graph is about trees.

Step 3 Decide how many each tree will stand for. Having each 🌳 stand for 10 trees works well, given the data.

Step 4 Draw symbols to show the data.

Trees in the Park

Kind of Tree	Number of Trees
Elm	🌳 🌳 🌳 🌳
Maple	🌳 ½🌳
Oak	🌳 🌳 ½🌳
Pine	🌳 🌳 🌳 🌳 🌳

Key: 🌳 = 10 trees

Use the graph above to solve the problems.

1. How many trees did James see in all?

   130 trees

2. How many more pine trees than maple trees did James see?

   35

3. Suppose that James saw 5 more elm trees. How can that change be shown on the graph?

   You will need to add a half of tree.

Put It Together

Use what you know about picture graphs to answer the questions.

1. Lavina took a survey. She asked her classmates their favorite pizza toppings. Her data is shown below. Use the data from the table to complete the picture graph.

Favorite Pizza Toppings

Answer	Tally
Mushroom	𝍸 𝍸 I
Pepperoni	𝍸
Spinach	𝍸 III

Favorite Pizza Toppings	
Mushroom	●●●●●◖
Pepperoni	◯◯◖
Spinach	◯◯◯◯

Key: ● = 2 people

Use the graph below to solve the problems. Share your solutions with a classmate.

2. How many more eggs were collected on Friday than on Wednesday?

8 eggs

3. Mrs. Greene collects 24 eggs on Saturday. How many symbols are needed to show this on the picture graph?

6 symbols.

4. Compare the number of eggs collected on Monday to the number collected on Wednesday and Friday combined.

the number collected on Wednesday and Friday combined is equal to Monday's eggs.

Eggs Collected in a Week

Day	Number of Eggs
Monday = 32	◯◯◯◯◯◯◯◯
Wednesday = 12	◯◯◯
Friday = 20	◯◯◯◯◯

Key: ◯ = 4 eggs

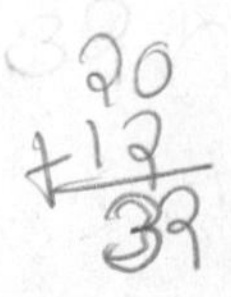

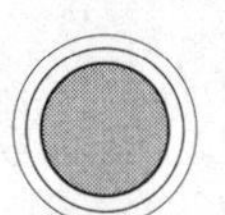

Make It Work

Answer the questions below.

Use the picture graph for problems 1–5.

BALLOONS SOLD

Student	Number of Balloons Sold
Paula	
Justin	
Ramon	
Andrea	

KEY
Each = 2 balloons

1. Which student sold 5 balloons?

A. Paula

B. Justin

C. Ramon

D. Andrea

2. How many balloons did Justin and Andrea sell in all?

A. 7 balloons

B. 10 balloons

C. 14 balloons

D. 17 balloons

3. Which student sold 3 more balloons than Ramon?

Andrea

4. Fredrico sells 9 balloons. How would you change the graph to include the balloons Fredrico sells?

I would draw 4 balloons and a half.

5. Use your own paper to draw the balloon picture graph using the key = 4 balloons.

Drawing and Interpreting Scaled Bar Graphs

3.MD.3 Draw a scaled picture graph and a scaled bar graph to represent a data set with several categories. Solve one- and two-step "how many more" and "how many less" problems using information presented in scaled bar graphs. *For example, draw a bar graph in which each square in the bar graph might represent 5 pets.*

Real World Connections

Key Words

bar graph
vertical
horizontal
scale

A **bar graph** shows data using bars of different heights. Like picture graphs, bar graphs are often used in newspapers, magazines, and in your school books. Bar graphs are often used more than pictographs because it is often easier to represent a data set using bars of varying heights than drawing many symbols for a picture graph. The bars in a bar graph can either be **vertical** (the bars go up) or **horizontal** (the bars go from left to right).

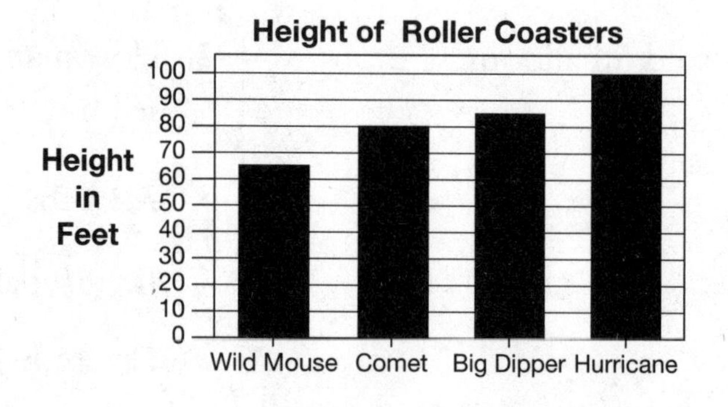

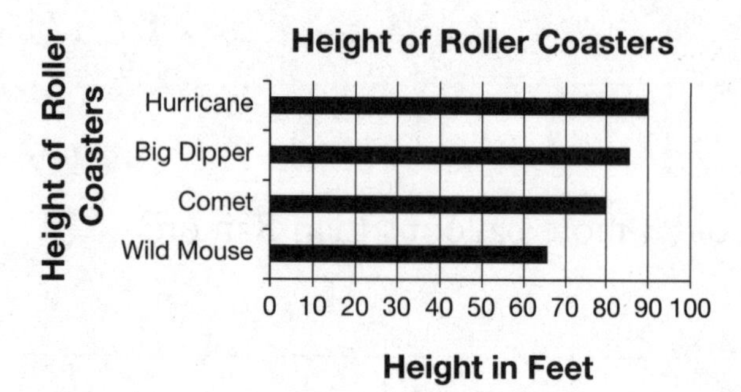

The **scale** is the equally spaced marks along the graph. The scale is numbered to help you read the number each bar shows.

Look at the bar for the Comet roller coaster on either graph. The bar ends at a line. Follow the line to the scale to find the height of the roller coaster. The Comet is 80 feet high.

Now look at the bar for the Big Dipper roller coaster. The bar ends halfway between the line for 80 feet and the line for 90 feet. This means the height is 85 feet, since 85 is halfway between 80 and 90.

Take It Apart

Follow these steps to make a bar graph of the tally chart.

Cory picked cards out of a bag and recorded each card she picked on the tally table shown.

Step 1 Choose a title that tells about the graph.
Pick a Card Results is a good choice because it tells what the graph is about.

Step 2 List the four different cards along the bottom of the graph: Star, Heart, Triangle, Square.

Step 3 Write a scale with numbers along the left side of the graph. Start with 0. The greatest number should be equal to or greater than the largest data number.

Step 4 Draw bars to match the numbers of the data from the tally table.

Pick a Card Results

Star	||||
Heart	卌 卌
Triangle	卌 卌 |
Square	卌 ||

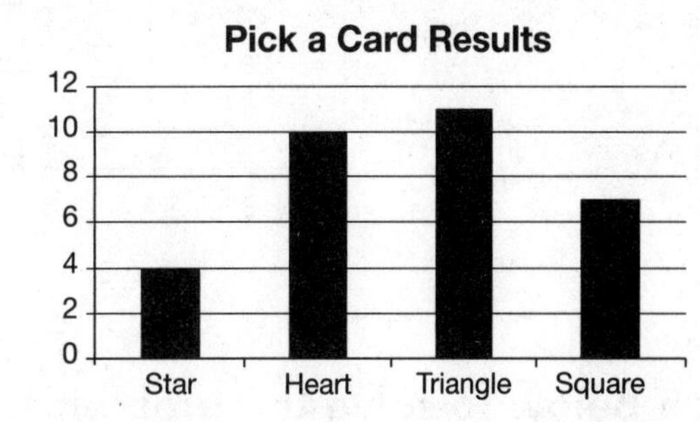

Use the graph above to solve the problems.

1. Which card did Cory pick most often?

Triangle

2. How many heart cards and triangle cards did Cory pick in all?

21

3. Did Cory pick more triangle cards and star cards or heart cards and square cards? Explain how you solved.

Cory picked more heart and square card. First, I add triangle and star. I got 15. then, I added heart and star. I got 17. 17 > 15

Put It Together

Use what you know about bar graphs to answer the questions.

1. Akim asked his classmates to vote for their favorite sports. His data is shown below. Use the data from the table to complete the bar graph.

Favorite Sports	
Sport	**Number of Votes**
Soccer	卌 卌 II
Lacrosse	卌 II
Football	卌 IIII
Volleyball	卌 卌

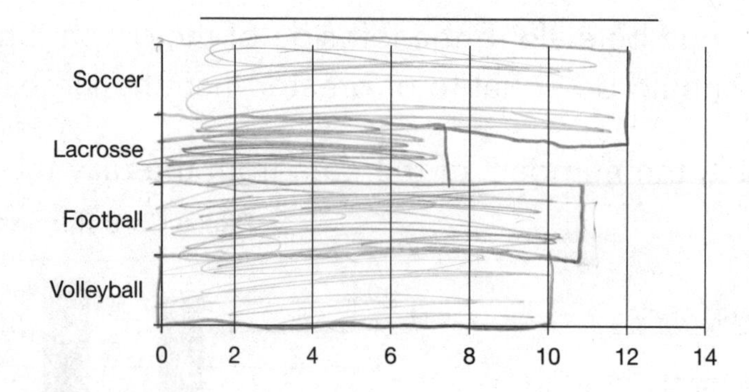

Use the graph below to solve the problems. Share your solutions with a classmate.

2. How many more votes did four square receive than tag?

4 votes

$8 - 4 = 4$

3. Which playground games received 5 or more votes?

Marbs, tetherball, and four squar.

4. Nine students voted for kickball. Describe how you would show this on the graph.

I would make a bar in the middle of eight and ten.

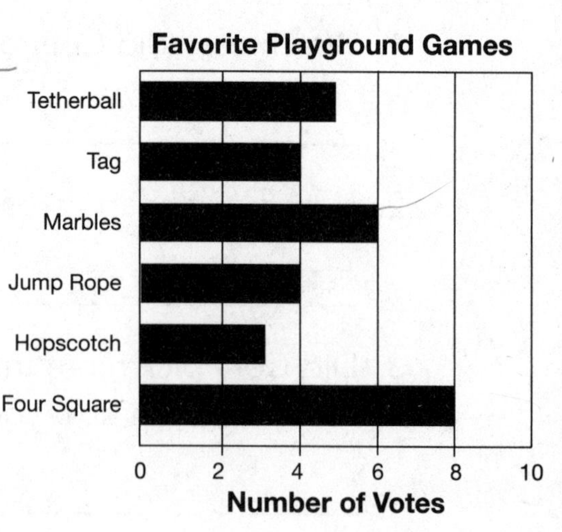

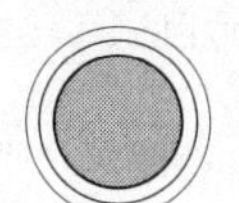

Make It Work

Answer the questions below.

Use the bar graph for problems 1–5.

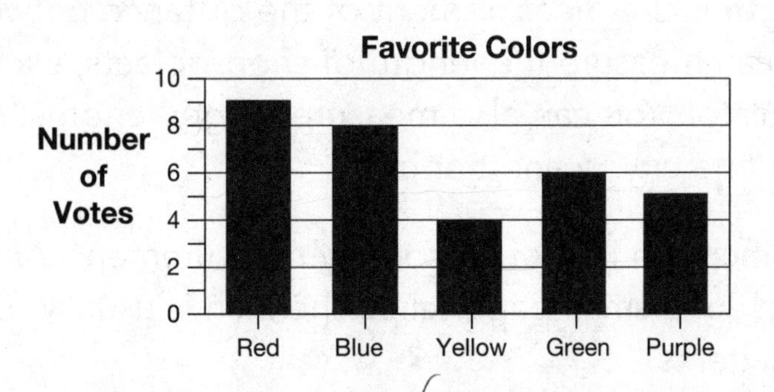

1. Which color had 2 more votes than yellow?

A. red

B. blue

C. green

D. purple

2. How many votes did red, yellow, and purple receive in all?

A. 6 votes

B. 18 votes

C. 19 votes

D. 20 votes

3. Which color received 3 fewer votes than blue?

Purple

4. Three students voted for orange. How can you change the graph to show this?

I would draw a bar in the middle of two a four.

5. Survey your classmates to find out their favorite colors. Then make a horizontal bar graph showing the data. Use your own paper for the graph.

Measuring Length to the Nearest Whole Inch

3.MD.4 Generate measurement data by measuring lengths using rulers marked with halves and fourths of an inch. Show the data by making a line plot, where the horizontal scale is marked off in appropriate units – whole numbers, halves, or quarters.

Real World Connections

Toolbox

Inch ruler

Key Words

length
inch
ruler
line plot

Length is the measurement of the distance between two points. You can measure the length of short objects, such as a crayon or calculator. You can also measure longer lengths, such as the distance from one city to another city.

The **inch** is a unit of customary measurement. An inch is about the length of a small paper clip. The inch is usually used to measure small items.

You can use a **ruler** to measure objects. This ruler is an inch ruler. Whole inches are labeled on the ruler.

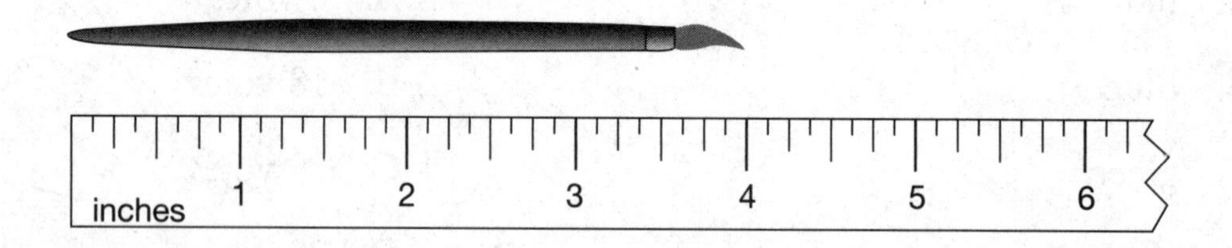

To measure to the nearest inch, line up one end of the object with the end of the ruler. Then find the 1-inch mark that is closest to the other end of the object.

The paintbrush is about 4 inches long.

A **line plot** is a graph that uses Xs above a number line to show data. You can record measurement data on a line plot. The line plot below shows the length of the paintbrush. You can record multiple pieces of data on a line plot.

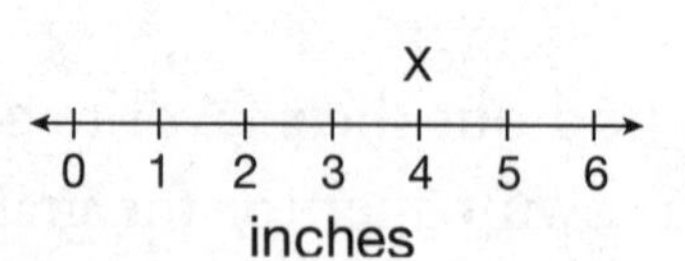

Take It Apart

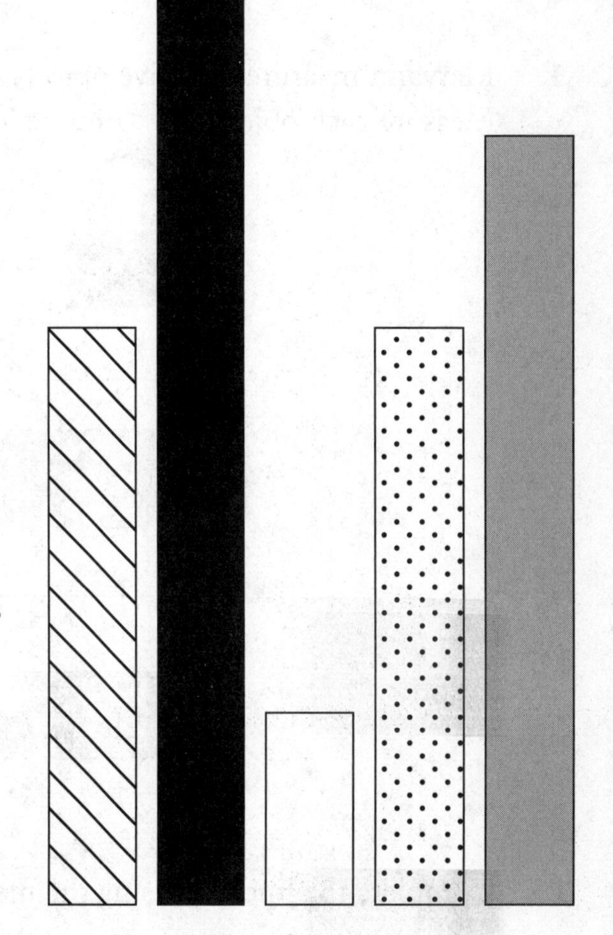

Jasmine measured the length of each of five ribbons. She recorded the length of each ribbon on a line plot.

Step 1 Measure the ribbons using the inch ruler. When the objects are vertical, either turn the page to measure or turn the ruler.
The striped ribbon is 3 inches long.
The black ribbon is 5 inches long.
The white ribbon is 1 inch long.
The dotted ribbon is 3 inches long.
The gray ribbon is 4 inches long.

Step 2 Decide the scale of the line plot. The lengths range from 1 inch to 5 inches, so using a scale from 1 to 5 will work.

Step 3 Draw Xs on the line plot to match the measurement data.

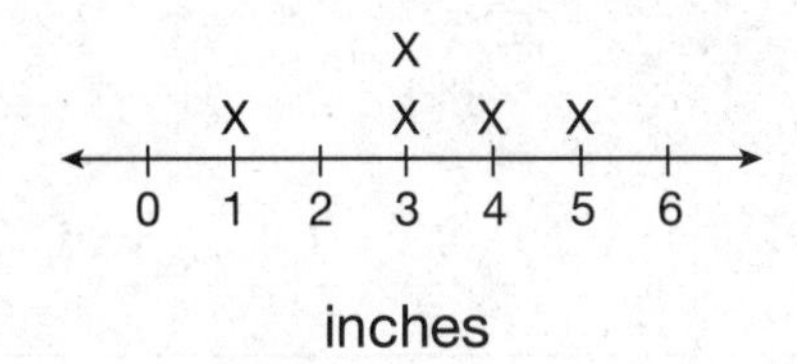

Use your ruler and what you know about measuring to the nearest inch to solve the problems.

1. How long is the eraser, to the nearest inch?

0 inches 2

____

2. Pedro has a bookmark that is 4 inches long. Draw a line that is the same length as Pedro's bookmark.

____

Put It Together

1. Maryann measured the five objects shown below to the nearest inch. Measure each object and write the length on the line below the object.

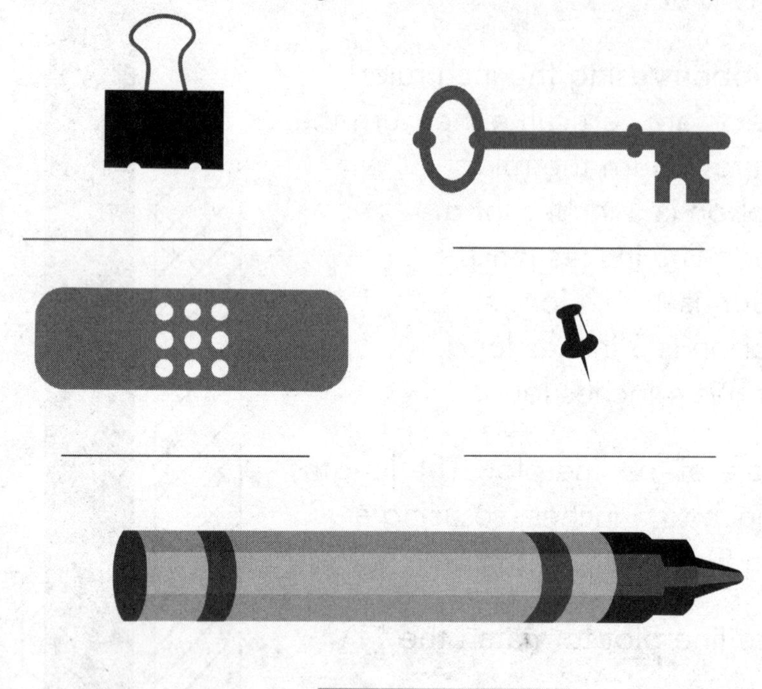

2. Complete the line plot using the measures from question 1.

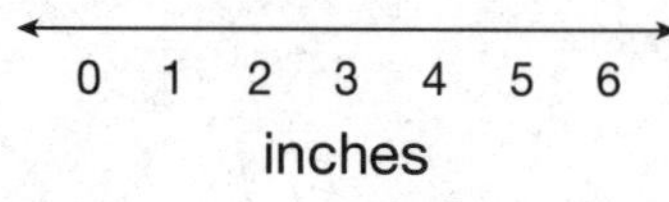

Use what you know about measuring length and using line plots to solve the problem. Share your solution with a classmate.

3. Mrs. Rios needs 5 inches of yarn for a sewing project. Is the piece of yarn shown below long enough? Explain why or why not.

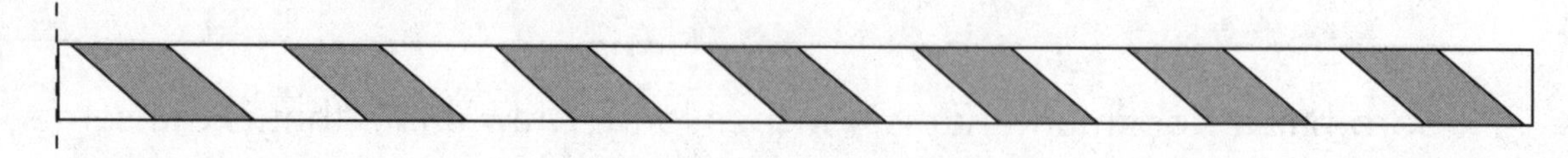

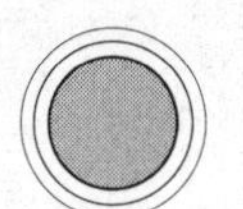

Make It Work

Answer the questions below. Use your inch ruler, when needed.

1. About how long is the paper clip?

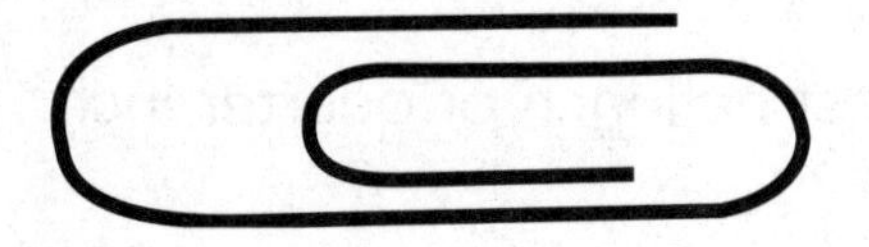

A. 1 inch

B. 2 inches

C. 3 inches

D. 4 inches

2. About how long is the ribbon?

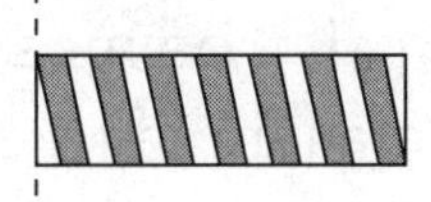

A. 1 inch

B. 2 inches

C. 3 inches

D. 4 inches

3. Marcy needs a piece of rope that is exactly 4 inches long. Circle the piece of rope she uses.

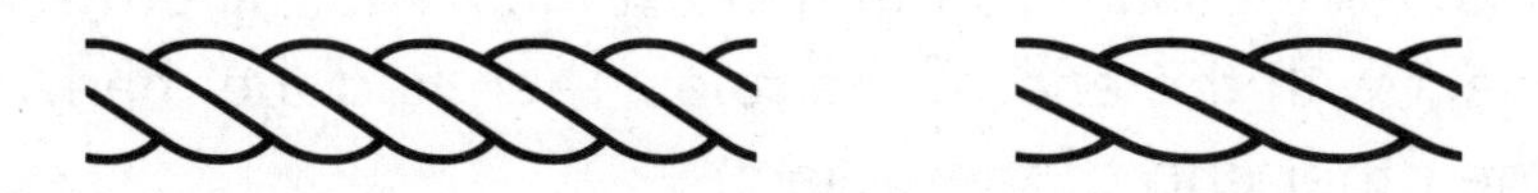

4. A small paper clip is about 1 inch long. Why is it better to use a ruler than paper clips to measure length?

____

5. Measure the length of five objects in your desk to the nearest inch. Record each object and its measurement. Then make a line plot showing the measurements. Use your own paper for this problem.

____

Lesson 29 Measuring Length to the Nearest Whole, Half, or Quarter Inch

3.MD.4 Generate measurement data by measuring lengths using rulers marked with halves and fourths of an inch. Show the data by making a line plot, where the horizontal scale is marked off in appropriate units – whole numbers, halves, or quarters.

Real World Connections

Toolbox

Inch ruler

Key Words

half inch

quarter inch

In the last lesson, you learned that an inch is a unit of customary measurement used to measure length.

Objects can also be measured to the nearest half inch or quarter inch using the smaller marks on an inch ruler.

The line halfway between two whole numbers is a **half inch**. The **quarter inch** marks are halfway between a whole number mark and the half inch mark.

The ruler below shows the half inch and quarter inch marks.

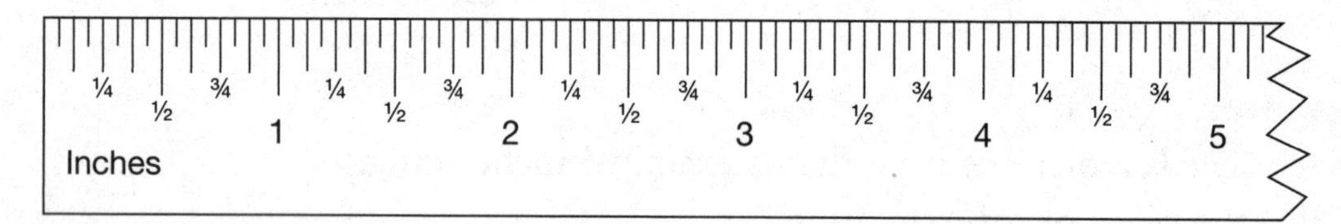

On an actual ruler, the half inch and quarter inch marks are not labeled. You need to learn the position of these marks to find the correct measurement.

To measure to the nearest half inch or quarter inch, you follow the same steps as you do to measure to the nearest inch. First, line up one end of the object with the end of the ruler. Then find the mark that is closest to the other end of the object.

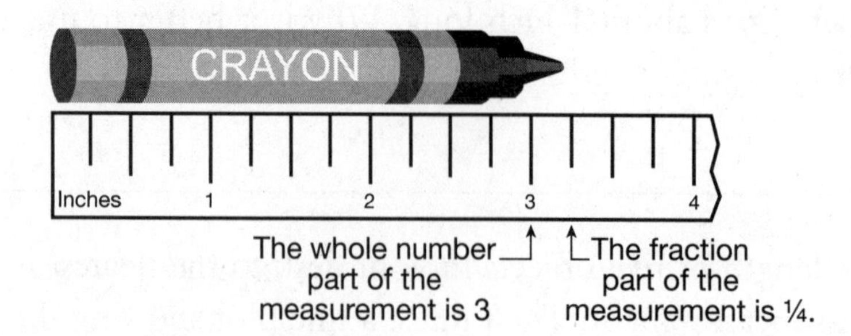

The crayon is $3\frac{1}{4}$ inches long.

Take It Apart

Chris measured the length of each of five strings to the nearest half inch. He then recorded the length of each string on a line plot.

Step 1 Measure each string using the inch ruler.

The first string is $1\frac{1}{2}$ inches long.

The second string is $3\frac{1}{2}$ inches long.

The third string is $2\frac{1}{2}$ inches long.

The fourth string is $1\frac{1}{2}$ inches long.

The fifth string is $\frac{1}{2}$ inch long.

Step 2 Decide the scale of the line plot. Since the lengths are to the nearest half inch, the scale of the line plot needs to show the half inch measures as well as the whole inch measures.

Step 3 Draw Xs on the plot to match the measurement data.

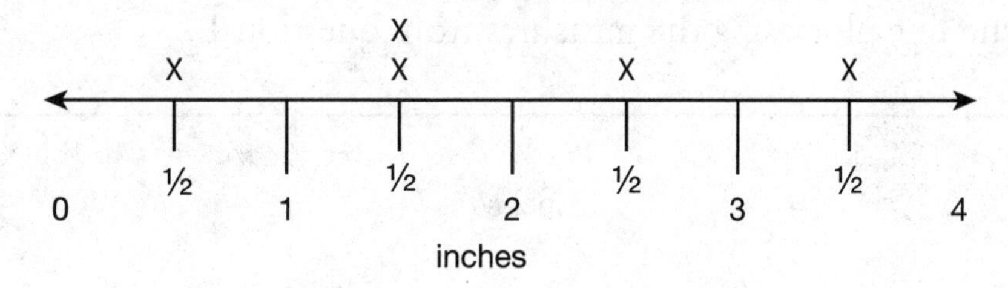

Use your ruler and what you know about measuring to the nearest half inch and quarter inch to solve the problems.

1. How long is the ribbon, to the nearest quarter inch?

____

2. Olivia measures a crayon using an inch ruler. The end of the crayon is halfway between the 3 inch mark and the 4 inch mark. How long is the crayon?

____

Put It Together

1. Measure the five ribbons below to the nearest quarter inch. Measure each object and write the length on the line below the object.

2. Complete the line plot using the measures from question 1.

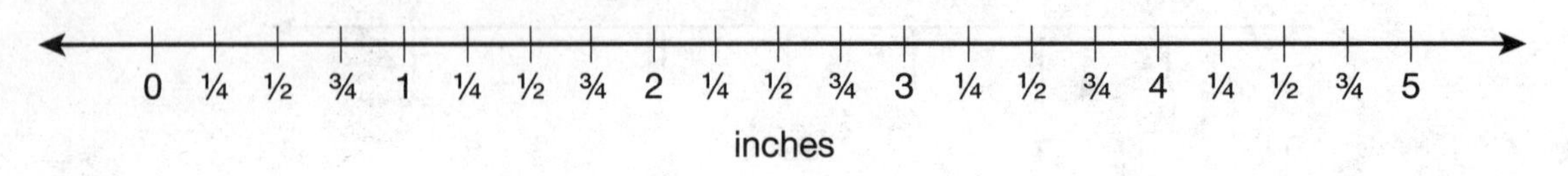

Use what you know about measuring to the nearest half inch and quarter inch to answer the problem below. Share your solution with a classmate.

3. Describe where you find the $4\frac{3}{4}$ mark on an inch ruler.

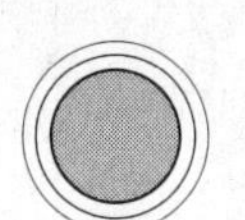

Make It Work

Answer the questions below. Use your inch ruler, when needed.

1. How long is the bug to the nearest half inch?

A. $\frac{1}{2}$ inch

B. $1\frac{1}{2}$ inches

C. 2 inches

D. $2\frac{1}{2}$ inches

2. How tall is the stamp to the nearest quarter inch?

A. $\frac{3}{4}$ inch

B. $1\frac{1}{4}$ inches

C. $1\frac{3}{4}$ inches

D. $2\frac{1}{4}$ inches

3. A worm is $2\frac{3}{4}$ inches long. Draw the worm above the ruler to show how to measure it to the nearest quarter inch.

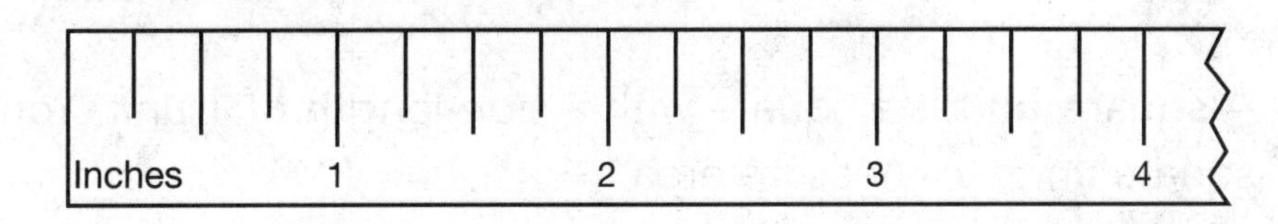

____

____

4. A student draws a blue line that is $5\frac{1}{2}$ inches long. Then below it he draws a red line that is $\frac{1}{4}$ inch longer. How long is the red line?

____

5. Measure the length of five objects in your classroom to the nearest half inch. Record each object and its measurement. Then make a line plot showing the measurements. Use your own paper for this problem.

____

Lesson 30 Introduction to Area

3.MD.5.a, 3.MD.5.b Recognize area as an attribute of plane figures and understand concepts of area measurement.

a. A square with side length 1 unit, called "a unit square," is said to have "one square unit" of area, and can be used to measure area.

b. A plane figure which can be covered without gaps or overlaps by *n* unit squares is said to have an area of *n* square units.

Real World Connections

Key Words

area

square unit

Area is the number of square units needed to cover a flat surface. You could find the area of any flat surface, such as the area of the cover of your math book or the area of your desk top.

Since the cover of your math book is smaller than your desk top, your math book cover will have an area that is less than the area of your desk top. Look at the picture below to help you compare the areas.

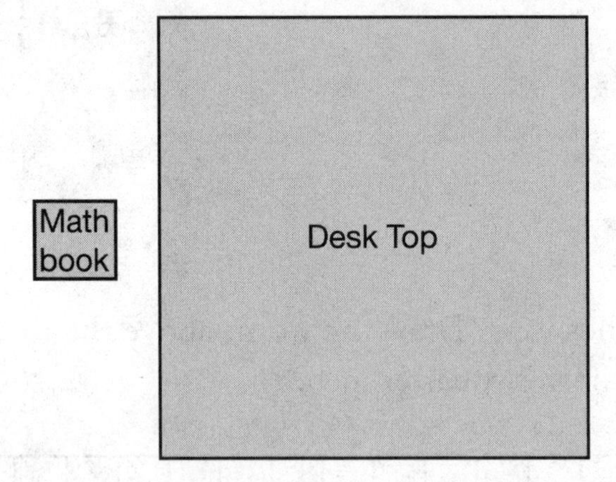

A **square unit** is a square with a side length of 1 unit. You use square units to measure area.

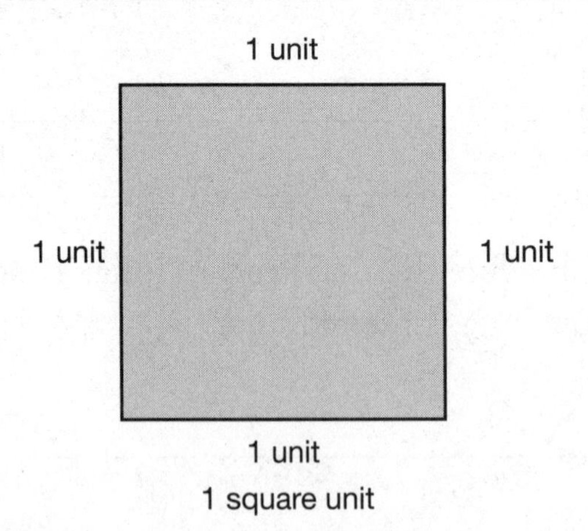

1 square unit

When you measure area, you must use units that are all the same size. Just like when you measure length, capacity, or mass, square units come in different sizes. They can be small, like the one shown above, or very large. As long as the unit is a square with a side length of 1 unit, it can be used to measure area.

Take It Apart

A student measures an index card by placing tiles on the index card as shown. What unit is the student using to measure the index card? What is the student measuring?

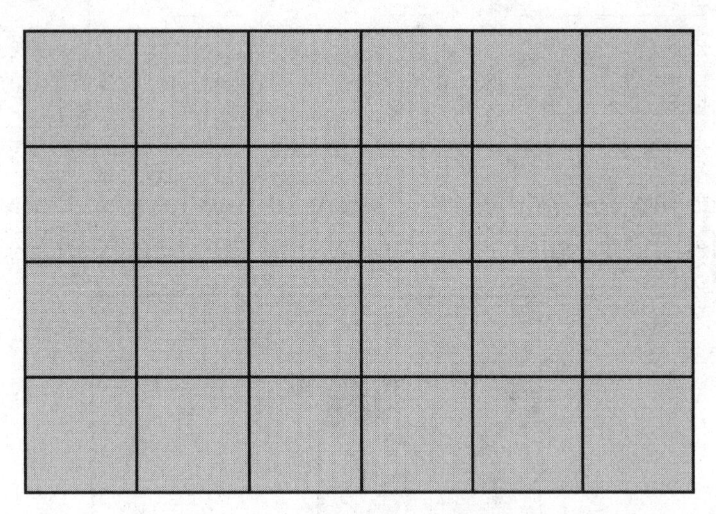

Step 1 Look at the tiles. Each one is a square and all of the tiles are the same size. The student is using square units for his measurement.

Step 2 Look at how the student is measuring the object. He is using tiles to cover the index card to find out how many square units are needed to cover the entire object. This means that the student is measuring area.

Use what you know about area to solve the problems.

1. Amber wants to find the area of an object. Circle the correct way to use square units to find area.

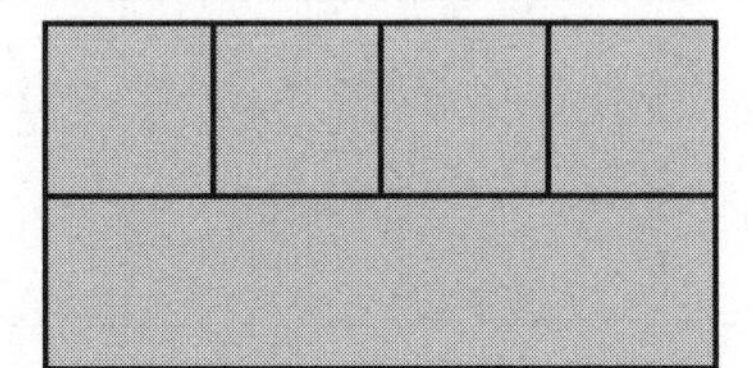

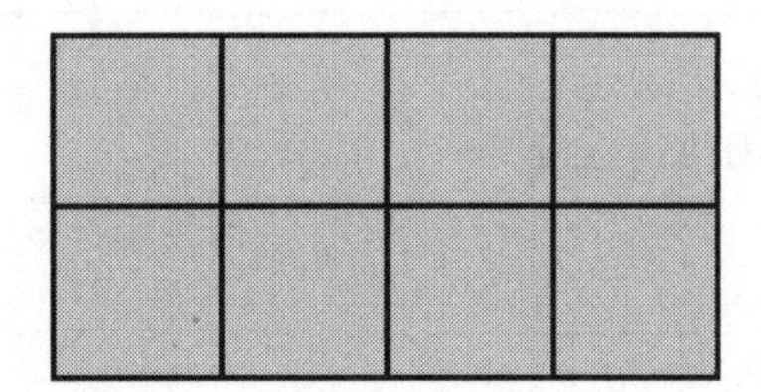

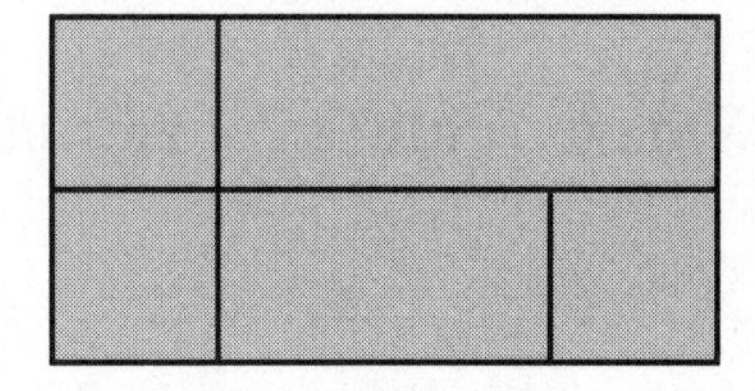

2. Tomas uses a ruler to measure how long a notebook is. Based on this measurement, he says the notebook has an area of 11 inches. Did Tomas measure area? Explain why or why not.

____

____

Put It Together

1. Circle the tile that could be used to find area.

 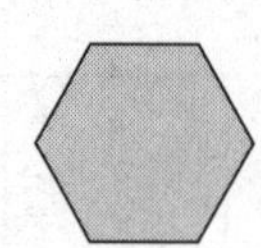 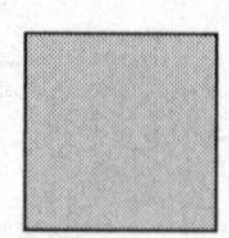 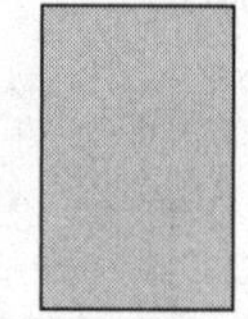

2. Carrie started placing tiles on the shape below to find its area. Draw lines to show the rest of the tiles Carrie will need to use to find the shape's area.

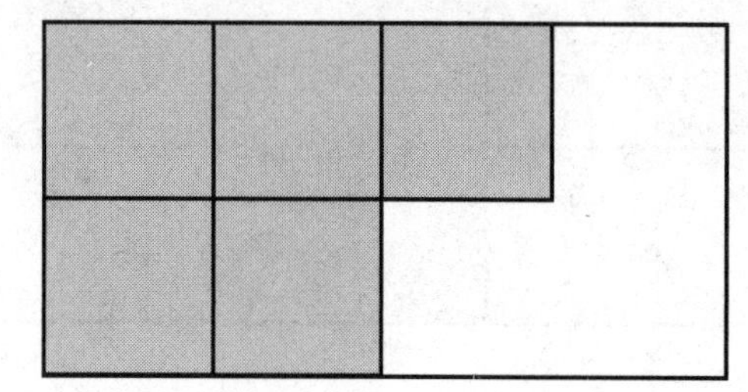

Use what you know about area to answer the problems below. Share your solutions with a classmate.

3. Amy says that she is going to find the area of a soup can. Explain why Amy is not able to do this.

____

____

4. Write a definition of area using your own words.

____

____

5. Compare and contrast length and area.

____

____

____

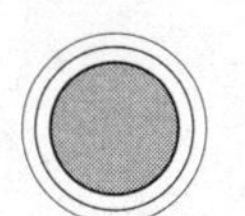

Make It Work

Answer the questions below.

1. Which unit is used to measure area?

A. inch

B. cubic unit

C. milliliter

D. square unit

2. A student covers a floor with large square tiles. The tiles are all the same size. What measurement is the student finding?

A. area

B. capacity

C. length

D. volume

3. Draw the other square units on the shape to show how to measure the area of the shape.

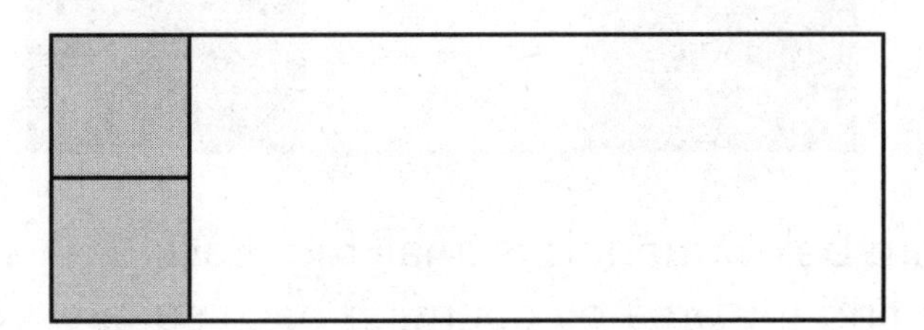

4. What is a square unit?

____

____

5. List five items in the room that you could measure the area of. Then circle if you would use a small square unit to measure the area or a large square unit to measure the area.

____________	small square unit	large square unit
____________	small square unit	large square unit
____________	small square unit	large square unit
____________	small square unit	large square unit
____________	small square unit	large square unit

Lesson 31 Measuring the Area of Plane Figures

3.MD.6 Measure areas by counting unit squares (square cm, square m, square in, square ft, and improvised units).

Real World Connections

Toolbox

square tiles

You can find the area of a flat surface by counting the number of square units needed to cover the surface.

Have you ever seen a tile floor? Maybe your classroom is covered in tiles that are all the same size. If you counted all the tiles needed to cover the floor, you would know the area of the floor in square units.

The figure below models a small rug. Each ■ = 1 square foot. You can find the area by counting each square.

1	2	3
4	5	6

The rug is 6 square units, so it has an area of 6 square feet.

When you count square units to find the area, you need to be sure to count each square once and only once. If you miss a square unit, or count a square unit twice, the area will not be correct.

Take It Apart

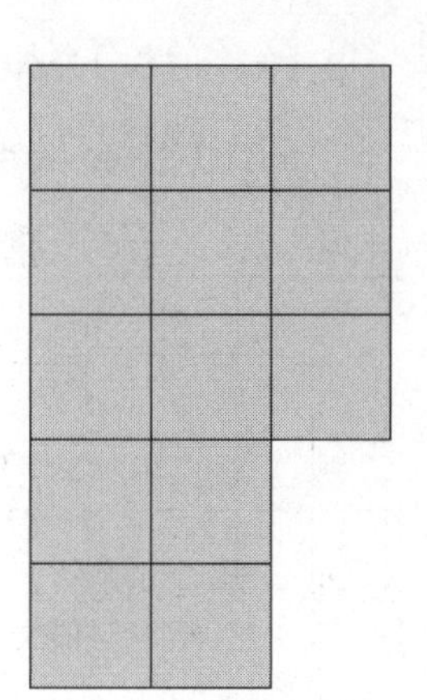

The diagram represents a room. Each ■ represents 1 square meter. What is the area of the room?

Step 1 Count the number of square units in the figure.

1	2	3
4	5	6
7	8	9
10	11	
12	13	

Note that the figure has some rows with fewer square units than the other rows. Be sure not to miscount.

Step 2 Write the area. Be sure to include the units in the answer.

The room has an area of 13 square meters.

Use what you know about area to solve the problems.

1. Each ■ represents 1 square cm. What is the area of the figure below?

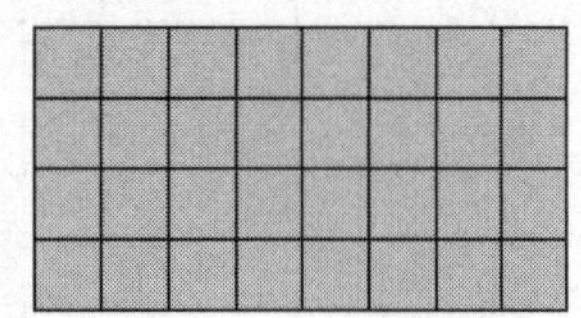

____

2. Each □ on the grid represents 1 square inch. Look at the figure drawn on the grid. Draw another figure on the grid that has the same area, but a different shape.

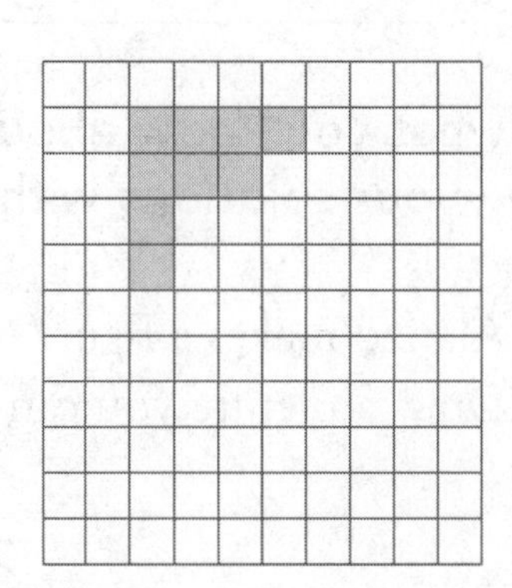

____

Put It Together

Find the area of each figure in square units.

1.

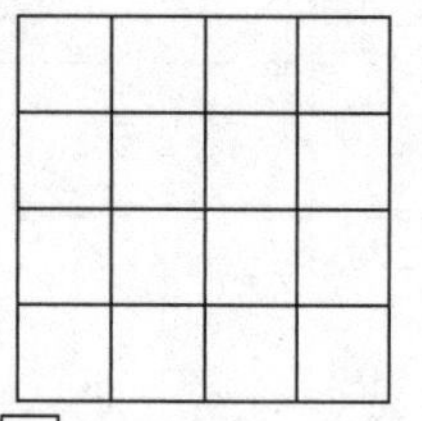

☐ = 1 square foot

____

2.

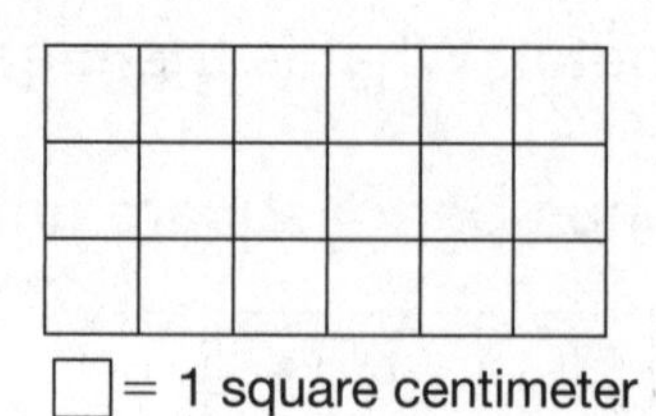

☐ = 1 square centimeter

____

3.

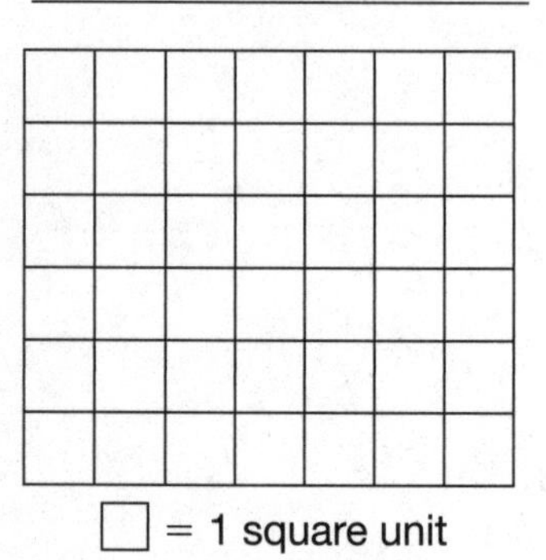

☐ = 1 square unit

____

4.

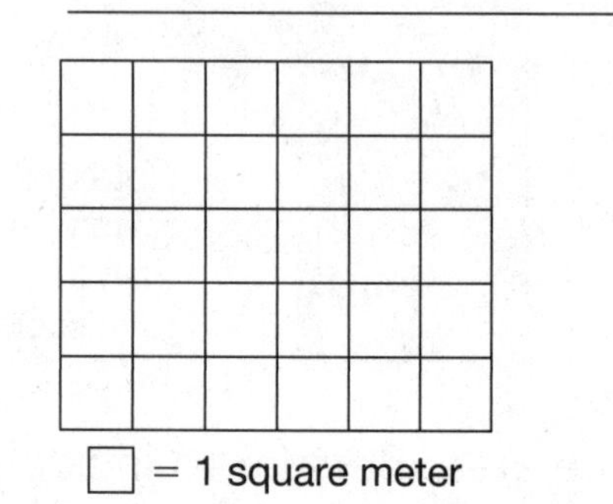

☐ = 1 square meter

____

Find the area of the shaded part of each figure in square units.

5.

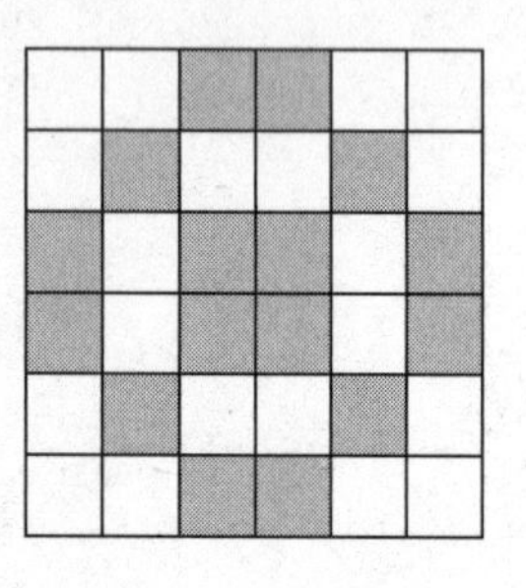

____

6.

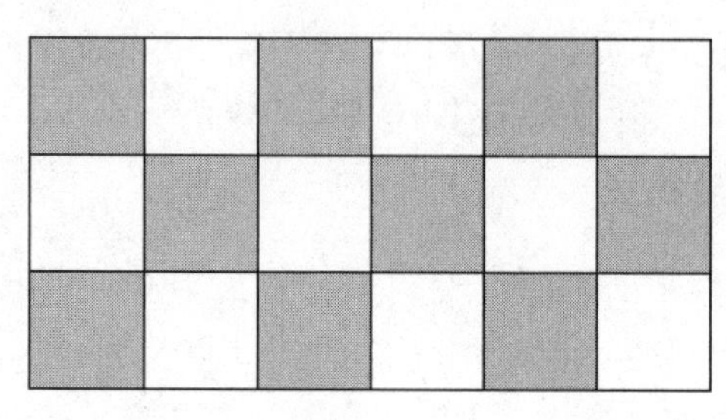

____

Use what you know about area to answer the problems below. Share your solutions with a classmate.

7. Alanzo makes a figure using square tiles. The figure has 3 rows. Each row has 4 tiles. Draw a picture you can use to help you find the area. Then find the area of the figure.

____

____

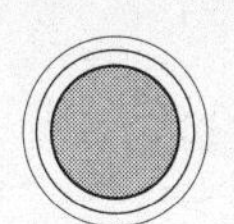

Make It Work

Answer the questions below.

1. What is the area of the figure below? Each □ = 1 square inch.

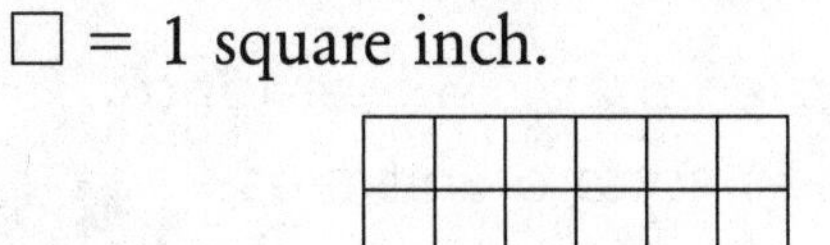

A. 6 square inches

B. 10 square inches

C. 12 square inches

D. 16 square inches

2. What is the area in square units of the shaded part of the figure below?

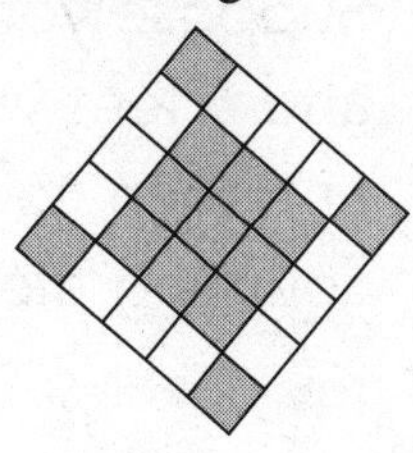

A. 25 **B.** 13

C. 12 **D.** 10

3. Draw a figure on the grid that has an area of 11 square units.

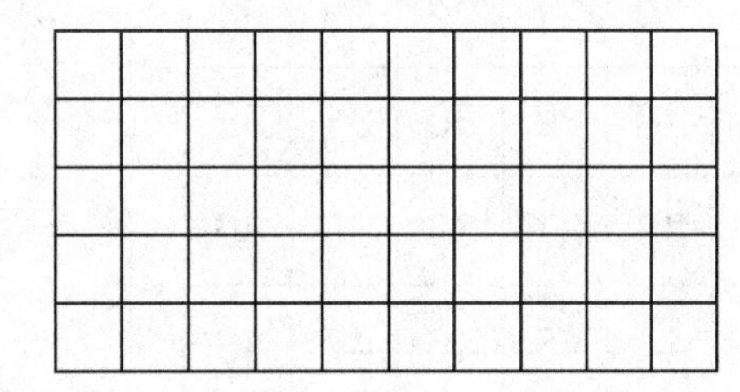

4. Donna drew four figures on grid paper. Circle the figure that has the greatest area.

A.

B.

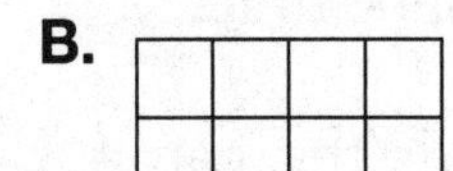

C.

D.

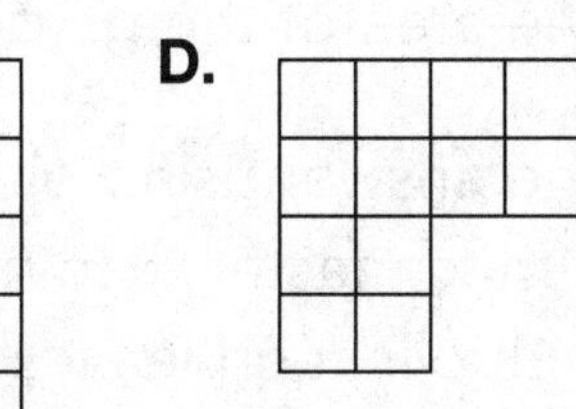

5. Use square tiles to find the areas of three objects in your classroom. Write the name of each object and the object's area on the lines below. Circle the object with the greatest area.

Object 1: ____________________ Area of Object 1: ____________________

Object 2: ____________________ Area of Object 2: ____________________

Object 3: ____________________ Area of Object 3: ____________________

Using Multiplication to Find Area

3.MD.7.a Find the area of a rectangle with whole-number side lengths by tiling it, and show that the area is the same as it would be found by multiplying the side lengths.

Real World Connections

Toolbox

square tiles

Suppose you need to find the area of a garden that is 8 feet long and 6 feet wide. You can make a model using square unit tiles and then count the tiles. You can also use multiplication instead of counting tiles to find the area of a rectangle.

Method 1 Make a model and count the tiles.

1	2	3	4	5	6	7	8
9	10	11	12	13	14	15	16
17	18	19	20	21	22	23	24
25	26	27	28	29	30	31	32
33	34	35	36	37	38	39	40
41	42	43	44	45	46	47	48

Method 2 Multiply.

To find the area of a rectangle, multiply the length by the width.

length × width = area

↓ ↓ ↓

$8 \times 6 = 48$

The area of the garden is 48 square units.

The answer using either method is the same, but using multiplication is much faster than making a model and counting. Plus, using multiplication leaves less room for error than when making the model or counting the tiles.

Take It Apart

Use multiplication to find the area of the rectangle.

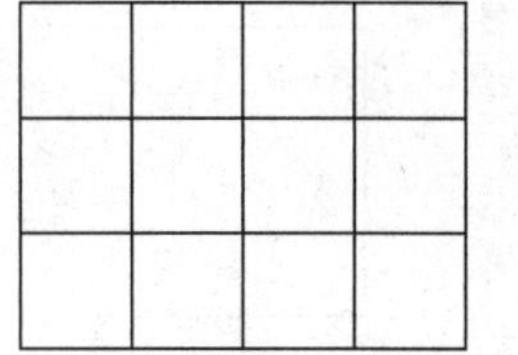

Step 1 Find the length and width of the rectangle by counting. The rectangle is 4 units long and 3 units wide.

Step 2 Multiply the length by the width.

$$4 \times 3 = 12$$

The area of the rectangle is 12 square units.

Use multiplication to find the area of the rectangle.

7 feet

5 feet

Step 1 Use the labels to find the length and width of the rectangle. The rectangle is 7 feet long and 5 feet wide.

Step 2 Multiply the length by the width.

$$7 \times 5 = 35$$

The area of the rectangle is 35 square feet.

Use what you know about area to solve the problems.

1. Carlos wants to find the area of a walkway that is 2 yards wide and 9 yards long. Describe two ways he can use to find the area.

____

____

2. A kitchen is 10 feet long and 7 feet wide. Show how you can use multiplication to find the area of the kitchen. Write the area using square units.

____

Put It Together

Find the area of each figure in square units.

1. 8 m, 6 m

______

2. 9 in., 4 in.

______

3. 12 ft, 9 ft

______

4. 8 cm, 8 cm

______

5. 11 yd, 7 yd

______

6. 15 yd, 12 yd

______

Use what you know about area to answer the problems below. Share your solutions with a classmate.

7. The area of a square is 9 square feet. What is the length of each side of the square?

______

8. The area of the bottom of a rectangular wagon is 8 square feet. One side of the wagon is 2 feet long. How long is the other side of the wagon?

______

9. Max makes an area model of a rectangle using 45 square unit tiles. Write a multiplication sentence that Max could use to find the area of the same rectangle.

______

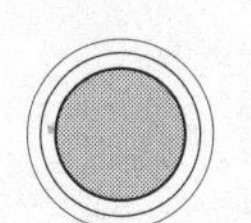

Make It Work

Answer the questions below.

1. What is the area of the rectangle in square inches?

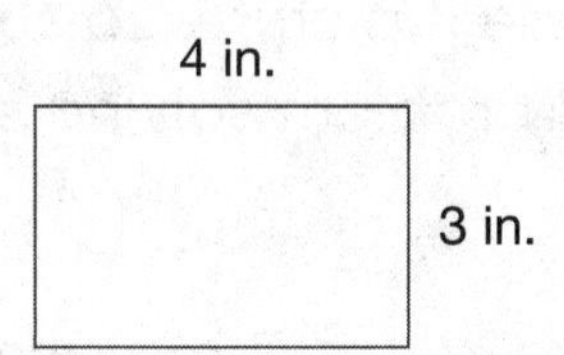

A. 7 **B.** 12

C. 24 **D.** 43

2. What is the area of the square in square yards?

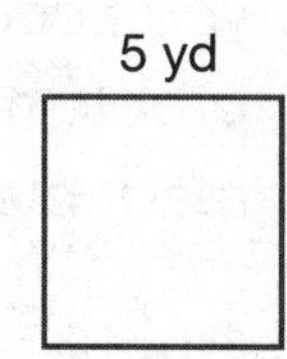

A. 10 **B.** 20

C. 25 **D.** 50

3. The paper shows how Jermaine found the area of a rectangle. Tell what mistake he made and explain how to solve it.

____

____

____

9 m

4 m

$9 + 4 = 13$
Area = 13 square meters

4. Suppose you know a rectangle has an area of 24 square units. What could be the side lengths of the rectangle? List the length and width of as many rectangles as possible.

____

5. Find four objects in your classroom that you can find the area of in square inches. Measure the length and width of each item to the nearest inch. Then use your measurements to calculate the area of each object.

____

Object	Length	Width	Area

Lesson 33 Finding Areas of Rectangles

3.MD.7.b Multiply side lengths to find areas of rectangles with whole-number side lengths in the context of solving real world and mathematical problems, and represent whole-number products as rectangular areas in mathematical reasoning.

Real World Connections

Real world problems about area often just have the measurements you need in the problem and do not include a picture. To solve these problems you need to follow the standard problem solving steps: read, plan, solve, and check.

On the playground there is a space to jump rope. The space is 4 yards wide and 12 yards long. The gym teacher wants to cover the space with padded tiles. Each padded tile equals 1 square yard. How many padded tiles will the gym teacher need?

Step 1 READ the problem and find the information you need.

- To find the number of tiles, you need to find the area of the jump rope space.
- The space is 4 yards wide and 12 yards long.

Step 2 PLAN to write a multiplication sentence to solve the problem.

Step 3 SOLVE

length × width = area

↓ ↓ ↓

12 × 4 = 48

Step 4 CHECK your work.

- Reread the problem to be sure you used the correct information.
- Think: Does 48 answer the question in the problem?

The gym teacher will need 48 tiles to cover the jump rope space.

Take It Apart

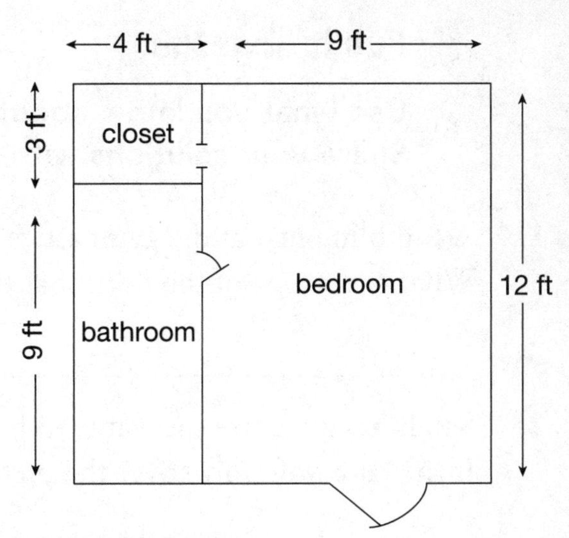

The floor plan shows Paulie's bedroom, bathroom, and closet.

The rug in Paulie's bedroom is 10 feet by 8 feet. How much floor space is not covered by the rug?

Step 1 READ You need to find the area of the floor not covered by the rug. This is a multi-step problem.

You need information from both the problem and the floor plan. The floor plan shows Paulie's room is 12 feet long and 9 feet wide. The problem says the rug is 10 feet long and 8 feet wide.

Step 2 PLAN First, find the area of Paulie's room and of the rug. Then subtract to find the area not covered by the rug.

Step 3 SOLVE

Area of Paulie's room: $12 \times 9 = 108$ square feet

Area of the rug: $10 \times 8 = 80$ square feet

Subtract the smaller area from the larger area. $108 - 80 = 28$ square feet

Step 4 CHECK if the answer makes sense. 28 square feet makes sense. There are 28 square feet of floor space not covered by the rug in Paulie's room.

Use what you know about area to solve the problems.

1. Paulie is going to put a tile floor in his bathroom. Each tile measures 1 square foot. How many tiles will Paulie need to cover the entire bathroom floor?

____

2. Paulie puts a dresser that is 3 feet wide and 1 foot deep in his closet. How much floor space is still open in his closet?

____

Put It Together

Use what you know about area to answer the problems below. Share your solutions with a classmate.

1. A tumbling mat at the gymnastics center is square. It measures 12 feet on one side. What is the area of the floor that the tumbling mat covers?

____

2. Sarah has a picture she wants to frame. The picture is 4 inches wide and 6 inches long. If the glass will only cover the picture, what will the area of the glass be?

____

3. The area of an index card is 15 square inches. One side is 3 inches long. How long is the other side of the card?

____

4. Dana's blanket is 2 meters wide and 5 meters long. What is the area of the blanket?

____

5. Mr. Hopkins is tiling the kitchen floor. Each tile measures 1 square foot. The kitchen is 9 feet long and 8 feet wide. How many tiles will Mr. Hopkins need for the entire kitchen?

____

6. A living room is 12 feet long and 10 feet wide. There is an area rug that is 9 feet long and 6 feet wide in the living room. How much floor space is not covered by the area rug?

____

7. Mrs. Chang bought enough mulch for a 24 square foot rectangular garden area. If one side of the garden measures 3 feet, what is the length of the other side of the garden?

____

8. A wall in Jose's bedroom is 8 feet tall and 10 feet long. He is painting the wall. So far he has painted a rectangle that is 3 feet by 7 feet. What is the area of the wall that Jose has left to paint?

____

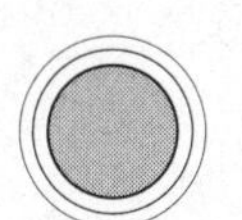

Make It Work

Answer the questions below. Use your inch ruler, when needed.

1. Mr. Breen uses 1 square meter carpet tiles to cover the floor of the playroom. The playroom is 8 meters wide and 11 meters long. How many carpet tiles will Mr. Breen use?

A. 19 carpet tiles

B. 36 carpet tiles

C. 80 carpet tiles

D. 88 carpet tiles

2. The third grade classroom is 7 yards long and 5 yards wide. What is the area of the classroom?

A. 12 square yards

B. 24 square yards

C. 35 square yards

D. 70 square yards

3. The area of a rectangular bedroom is 120 square feet. The length of the bedroom is 12 feet. What is the width of the bedroom?

____

4. Abby's bedroom has an area of 100 square feet. She has a rectangular rug on the floor. The area of the floor not covered by the rug is 55 square feet. What are the length and width of the rug?

____

5. Draw a floor plan, similar to the one on the second page of this lesson. Show at least 3 rooms and the length and width of each room. Then use your floor plan to find the area of each room.

____

Lesson 34 Exploring Area Through Tiling and Models

3.MD.7.c Use tiling to show in a concrete case that the area of a rectangle with whole-number side lengths a and $b + c$ is the sum of $a \times b$ and $a \times c$. Use area models to represent the distributive property in mathematical reasoning.

Real World Connections

Toolbox
cm grid paper

Key Words
area model
distributive property

Sometimes it helps to break apart a factor into smaller numbers to make it easier to multiply. An **area model** is a rectangular grid. The number of rows and columns in the area model show the factors you are multiplying. The total number of squares in the area model is the product of the factors.

The school marching band has 7 rows of students with 15 students in each row. How many students are in the marching band?

$7 \times 15 = ?$

$7 \times (10 + 5) = ?$

$(7 \times 10) + (7 \times 5) = ?$

$70 + 35 = 105$

$7 \times 15 = 105$

There are 105 students in the marching band.

This strategy is an example of the **distributive property**.
The distributive property states that when two addends are multiplied by the same factor, the product is the same as when each addend is multiplied by the factor and those products are added.

$$7 \times (10 + 5) = (7 \times 10) + (7 \times 5)$$

Take It Apart

You can use area models and the distributive property to solve multiplication problems. $4 \times 16 = ?$

Step 1 Draw an area model to show 4×16 on grid paper.

The model will have 4 rows with 16 squares in each row.

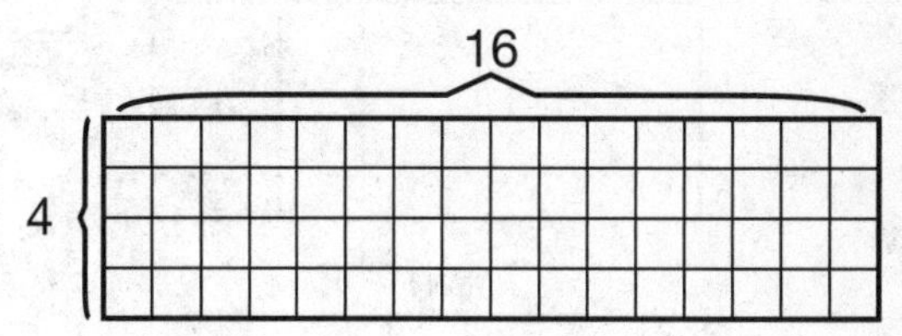

Step 2 Draw a line to separate the factor 16 into two factors that are easier for you to multiply.

You can use 10 and 6, 8 and 8, 11 and 5, or any other combination that equals 16.

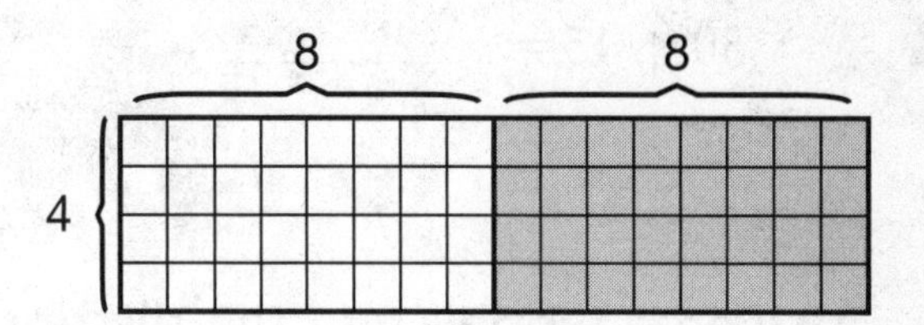

Step 3 Multiply to find the product of each section.

$4 \times 8 = 32$

$4 \times 8 = 32$

Step 4 Add the products to find the answer.

$32 + 32 = 64$

$4 \times 16 = 64$

Use area models and the distributive property to solve the problems.

1. $8 \times 13 = ?$

____

2. Write the multiplication problem that the area model represents. Then use the distributive property to find the product. Draw a line on the model to show how you divided the larger factor.

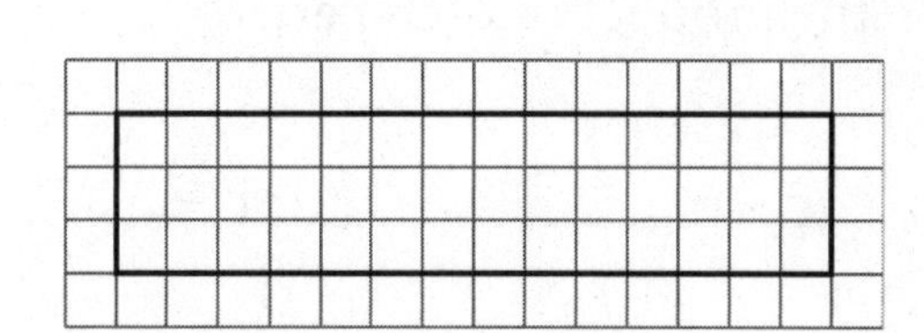

____

Put It Together

Complete the number sentences for each area model.

1.

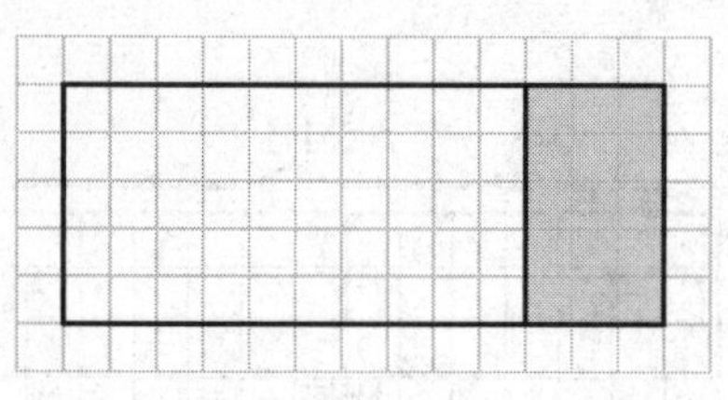

$5 \times 13 = ?$

$5 \times 10 =$ ____________

$5 \times 3 =$ ____________

$50 + 15 =$ ____________

$5 \times 13 =$ ____________

2.

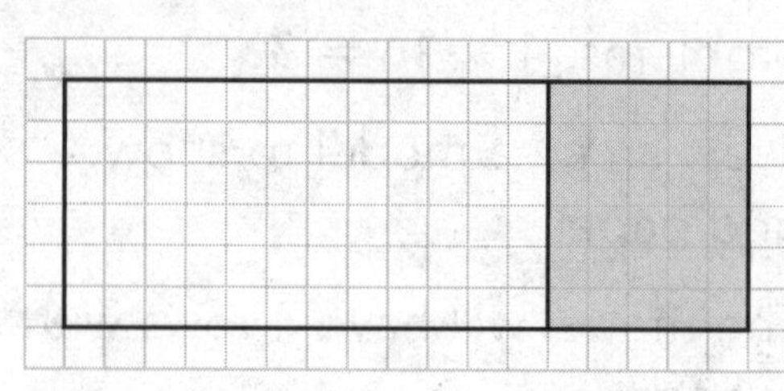

$6 \times 17 = ?$

$6 \times 12 =$ ____________

$6 \times 5 =$ ____________

$72 + 30 =$ ____________

$6 \times 17 =$ ____________

Use area models and the distributive property to find the product. Show your work.

3. 4×19 ____________

4. 6×13 ____________

5. 9×18 ____________

6. 5×15 ____________

Use what you know about area models and the distributive property to answer the problems below. Share your solutions with a classmate.

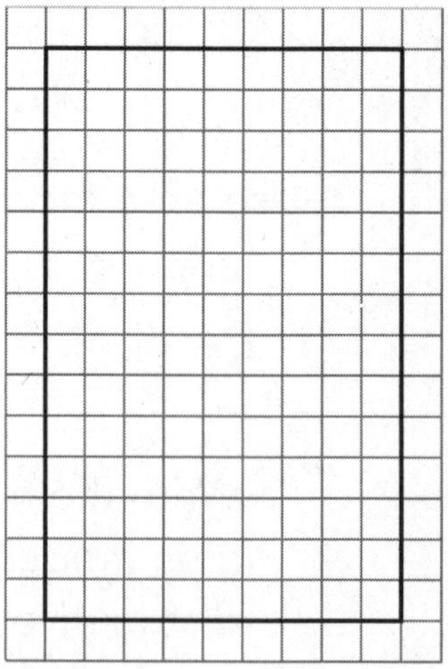

7. What factors are shown by the area model?

____

8. Draw a line to break the area model into two parts. Write multiplication sentences to show how to find the product of each part.

____

9. Write a number sentence for the area model.

____

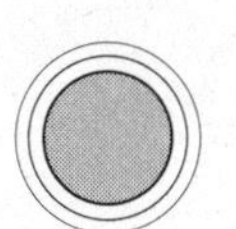

Make It Work

Answer the questions below.

1. Which of the following is shown by the area model?

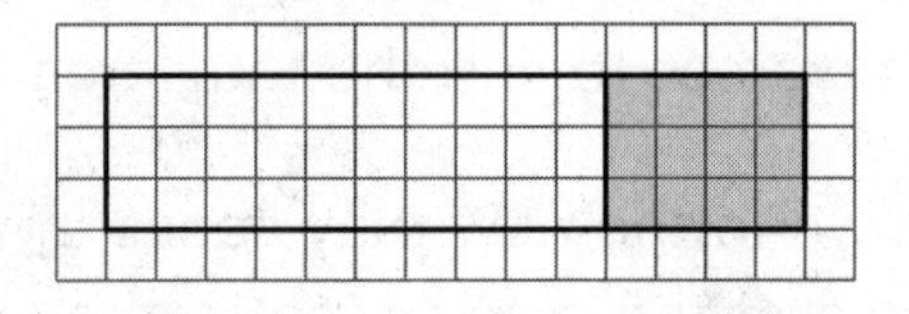

A. $3 \times 14 = (3 \times 10) + (3 \times 4)$

B. $3 \times 14 = (3 + 10) + (3 + 4)$

C. $3 \times 14 = (3 + 10) \times (3 + 4)$

D. $3 \times 14 = (3 \times 10) \times (3 \times 4)$

2. Pedro wants to find the product for 8×15. Which number sentence can he use to find the product?

A. $(8 \times 15) + (8 + 15)$

B. $(8 \times 10) + 5$

C. $(8 + 10) \times (8 + 5)$

D. $(8 \times 10) + (8 \times 5)$

3. The area model shows 7×13. Draw a line to divide the model into two parts. Then use the distributive property to find the product. Show your work.

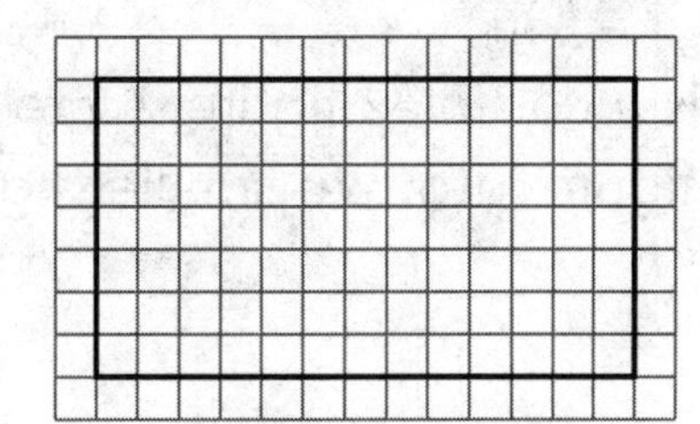

____

4. Frankie has 18 types of building blocks. He has 5 of each kind of block. Draw an area model on grid paper and use the distributive property to find how many blocks Frankie has in all.

____

5. Bob has to teach someone how to use area models and the distributive property to find 6×17. Write the steps to find the product. Include the product as part of your answer.

____

____

____

Lesson 35 Determining the Areas of Complex Figures

3.MD.7.d Recognize area as additive. Find areas of rectilinear figures by decomposing them into non-overlapping rectangles and adding the areas of the non-overlapping parts, applying this technique to solve real world problems.

Real World Connections

Key Word

complex figure

Sometimes you need to find the area of a complex figure. A **complex figure** is made of two or more figures. To find the area of a complex figure, you need to separate the figure into smaller figures, find the area of each smaller figure, and then add the areas to find the total area.

The town wants to put grass seed down in the new play space in the park. The town needs to know the area of the play space so they buy the right amount of seed. What is the area of the play space?

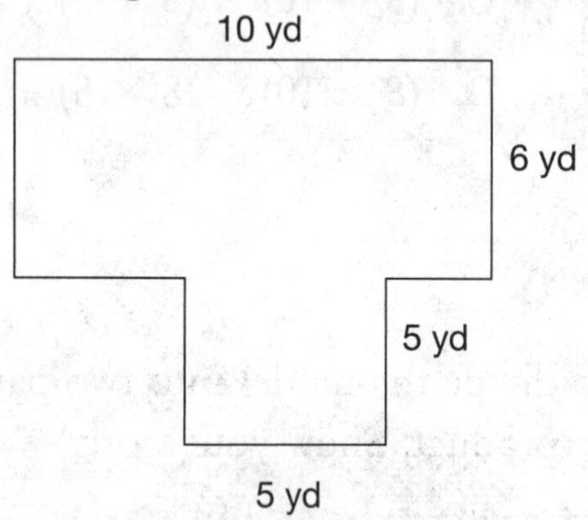

The play space is a complex figure, so to find the area you need to separate the figure into two smaller figures.

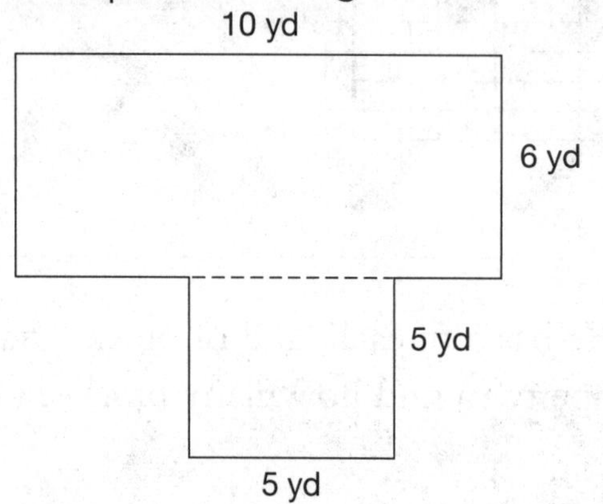

The play space can be separated into a square and a rectangle. To find the area, first find the area of the square and the rectangle. Then add both areas to find the area of the whole figure.

area of square: $5 \text{ yd} \times 5 \text{ yd} = 25$ square yards
area of rectangle: $6 \text{ yd} \times 10 \text{ yd} = 60$ square yards
area of complex figure: $25 \text{ sq yd} + 60 \text{ sq yd} = 85 \text{ sq yd}$

The play space has an area of 85 square yards.

Take It Apart

You can use some simple steps to find the area of a complex figure.

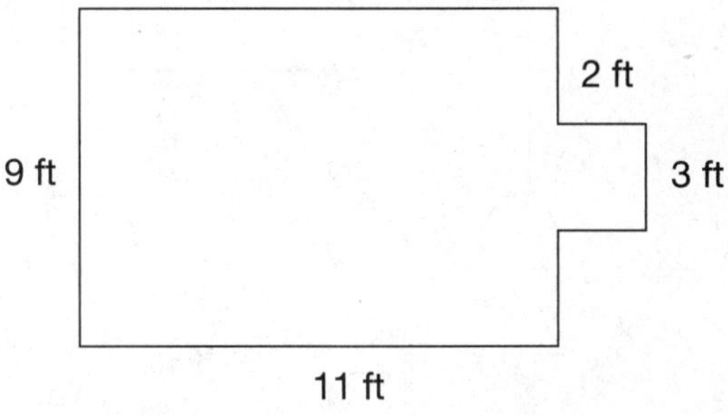

Greta wants to put new carpet in her bedroom. How many square feet of carpet will she need to buy to cover her entire bedroom floor?

Step 1 Look for a way to separate the complex figure into squares and/or rectangles.

You can divide this figure into two rectangles.

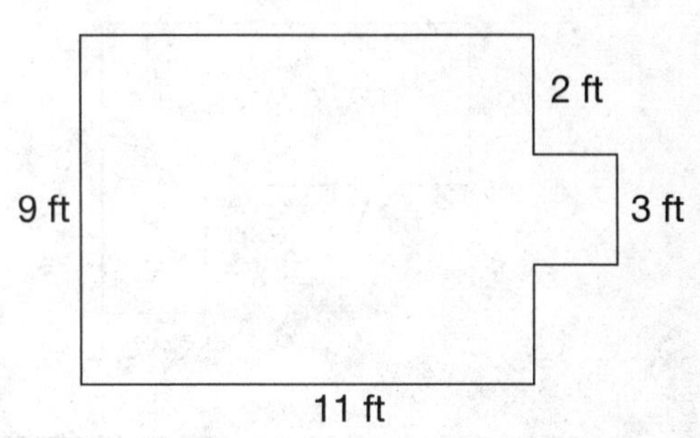

Step 2 Use multiplication to find the area of each rectangle.

$9 \text{ ft} \times 11 \text{ ft} = 99$ square feet
$3 \text{ ft} \times 2 \text{ ft} = 6$ square feet

Step 3 Add both areas to find the area of the whole room.

$99 \text{ sq ft} + 6 \text{ sq ft} = 105$ sq feet

Greta will need to buy 105 sq ft of carpet for her bedroom floor.

Use what you know about area of complex figures to solve the problems.

1. The gym coach needs tumbling mats to cover the area shown in the diagram to the right. What is the area that will be covered by the mats?

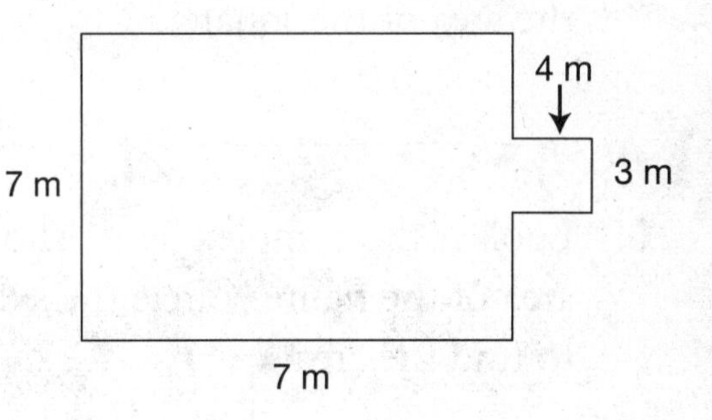

____

2. Draw lines to divide the complex figure to the right into three smaller figures. Then find the area of the figure.

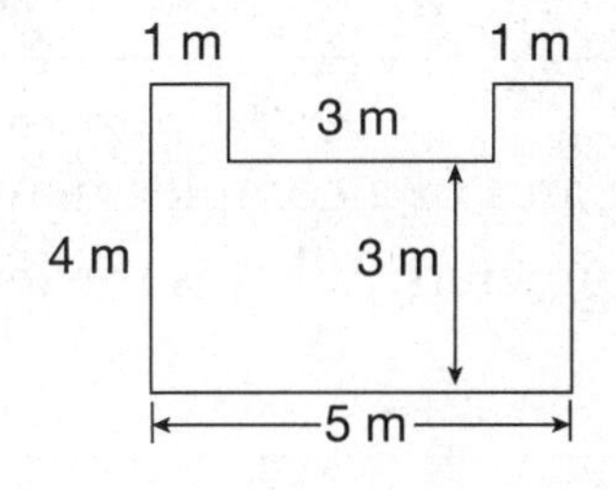

____

Put It Together

Find the area of each complex figure. Show your work.

1.

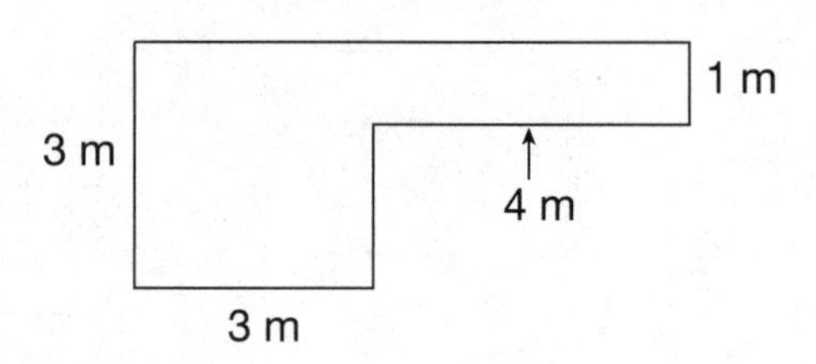

2.

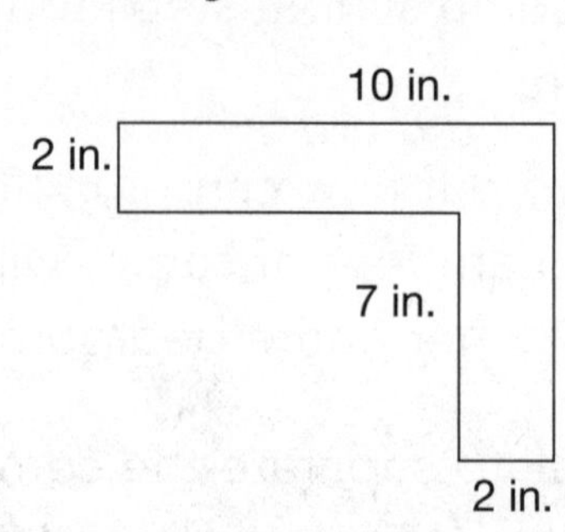

3.

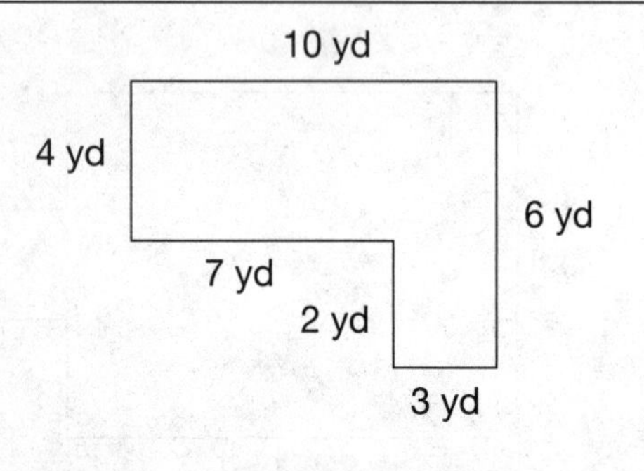

4.

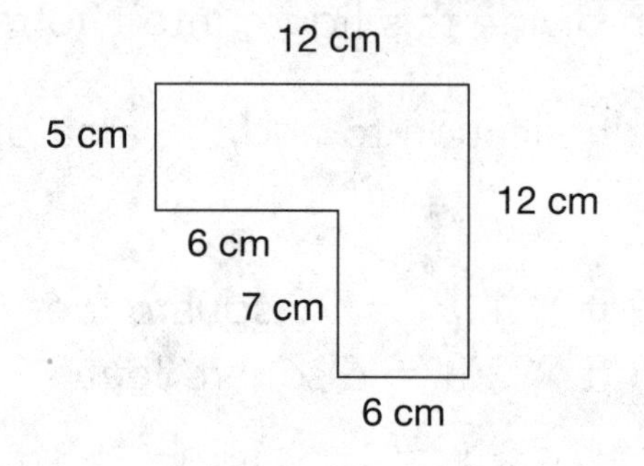

Use what you know about area of complex figures to answer the problems below. Share your solutions with a classmate.

5. A complex figure has an area of 52 square inches. The figure can be divided into a square and a rectangle. The rectangle is 12 inches long and 3 inches wide. What is the area of the square?

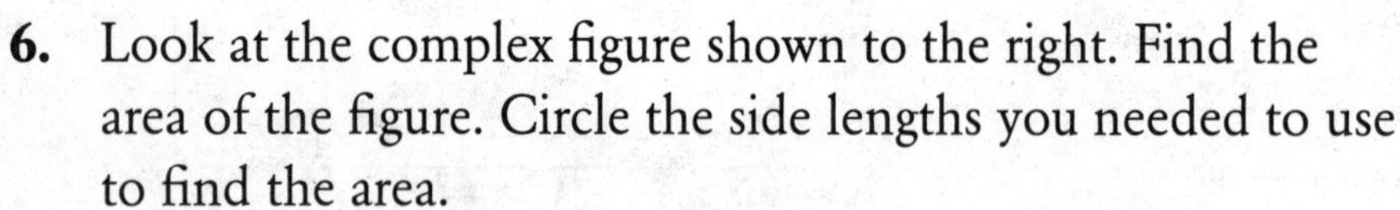

6. Look at the complex figure shown to the right. Find the area of the figure. Circle the side lengths you needed to use to find the area.

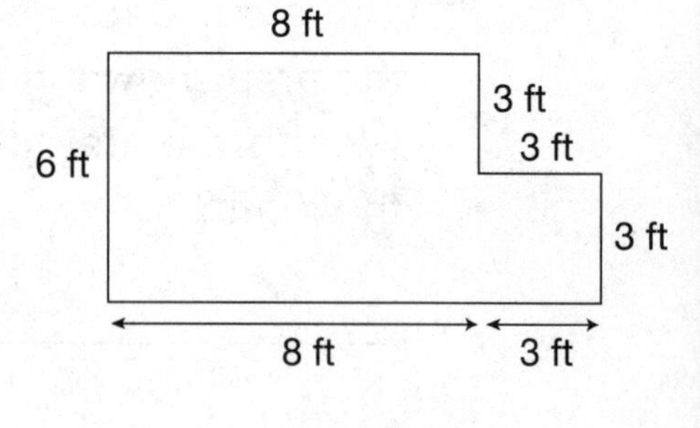

7. The area of a complex figure shown is 54 square centimeters. What is the length of the unknown side?

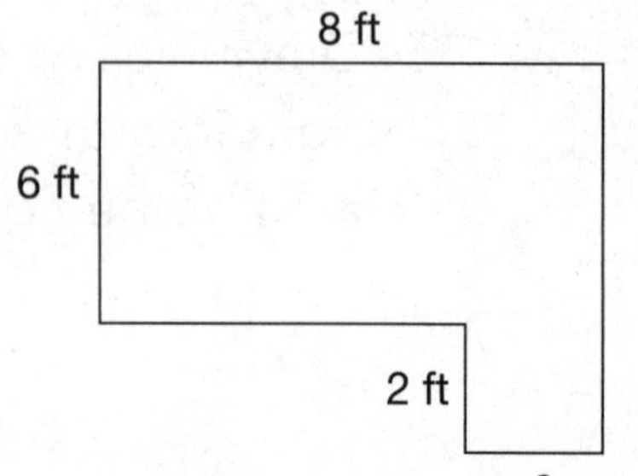

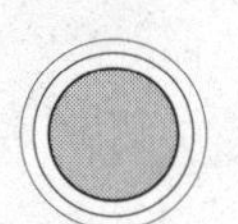

Make It Work

Answer the questions below.

1. What is the area of the figure?

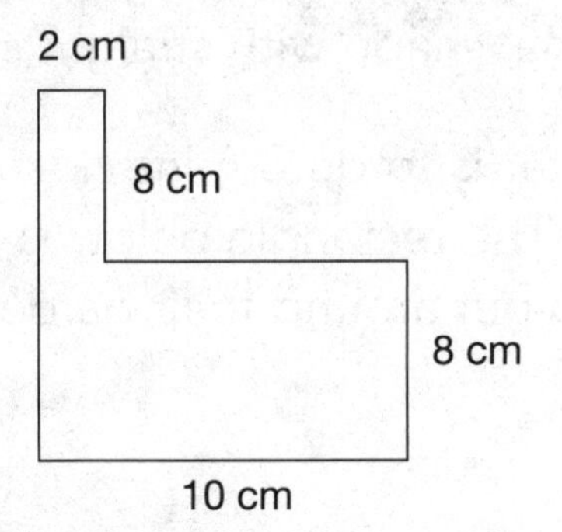

A. 16 square centimeters

B. 28 square centimeters

C. 80 square centimeters

D. 96 square centimeters

2. What is the area of the figure?

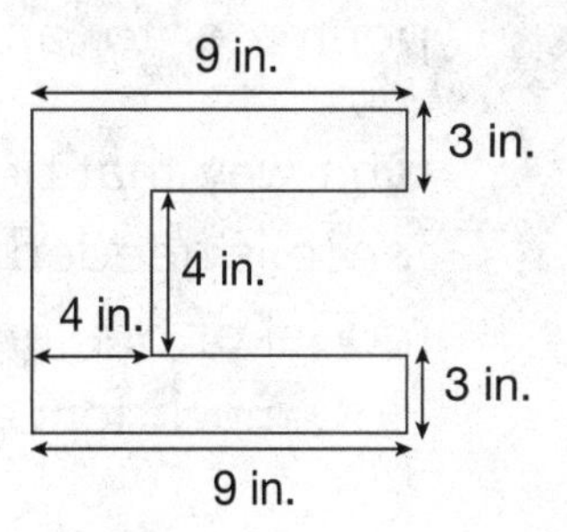

A. 70 square inches

B. 54 square inches

C. 32 square inches

D. 16 square inches

3. The area of a complex figure shown is 50 square feet. What is the length of the unknown side?

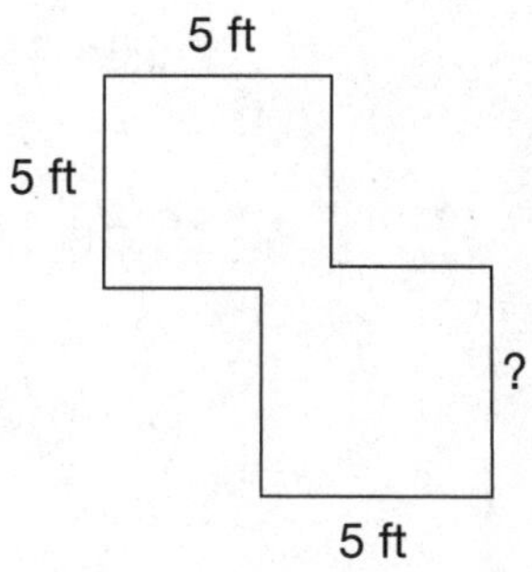

____

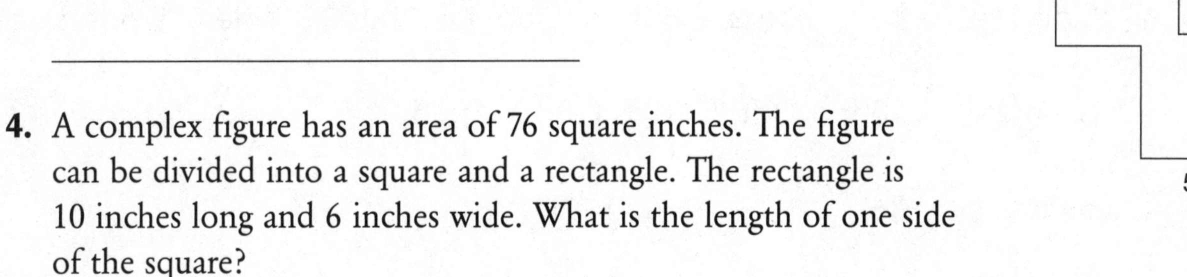

4. A complex figure has an area of 76 square inches. The figure can be divided into a square and a rectangle. The rectangle is 10 inches long and 6 inches wide. What is the length of one side of the square?

____

5. Look at your classroom. How could you find the area of your classroom? (Be sure to include entryways and closets.) Describe the steps you would need to take to find the area of the entire classroom.

____

____

Lesson 36 Solving Problems Involving Perimeter

3.MD.8 Solve real world and mathematical problems involving perimeters of polygons, including finding the perimeter given the side lengths, finding an unknown side length, and exhibiting rectangles with the same perimeter and different areas or with the same area and different perimeters.

Real World Connections

Key Word

perimeter

The distance around a figure is called the **perimeter.** You can find perimeter for any closed two-dimensional shape with straight sides.

One way that people often use perimeter is to determine how much fence is needed to go around a space. The rectangle below is a model of the fence the Wilsons want to put around their garden. How much fence do the Wilsons need?

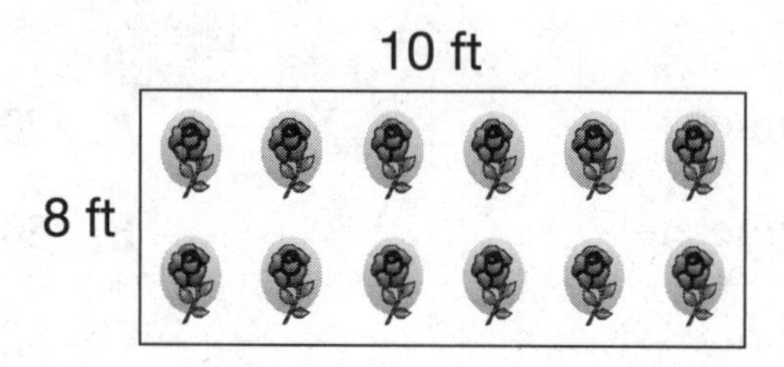

To find perimeter, find the lengths of each side. Note that the rectangle has 4 sides, but only 2 sides are labeled. Since opposite sides in a rectangle are the same length, you know that the length of side 1 = length of side 3 and the length of side 2 = length of side 4.

Side 1 = 10 ft Side 2 = 8 ft Side 3 = 10 ft Side 4 = 8 ft

perimeter = 10 ft + 8 ft + 10 ft + 8 ft

perimeter = 36 ft

The Wilsons need 36 feet of fencing to go around the garden.

The number of sides added together to find perimeter depends on the shape. For a hexagon, you would need to add 6 sides to find the perimeter. For a triangle you would need to add 3 sides.

Take It Apart

You can also use perimeter to find an unknown side length.

The perimeter of the triangle is 10 cm. What is the length of the unknown side?

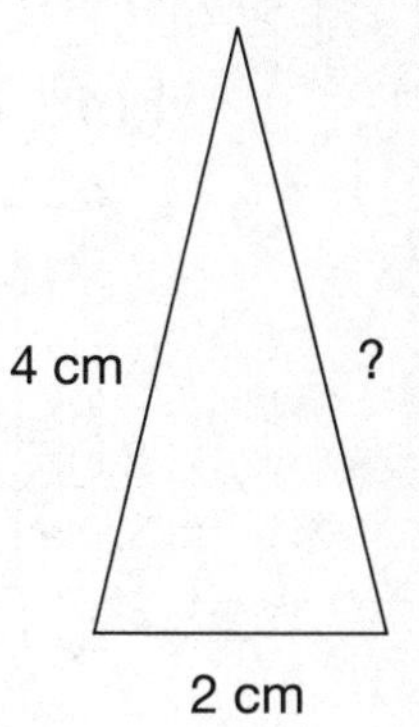

Step 1 Find the side lengths.

Side 1 = 4 cm Side 2 = 2 cm Side 3 = ?

Step 2 Subtract the known side lengths from the perimeter. The difference is the length of the unknown side.

10 cm − 4 cm − 2 cm = 4 cm

The unknown side length is 4 cm.

Use what you know about perimeter to solve the problems.

1. The perimeter of the triangle is 15 yards. What is the length of the unknown side?

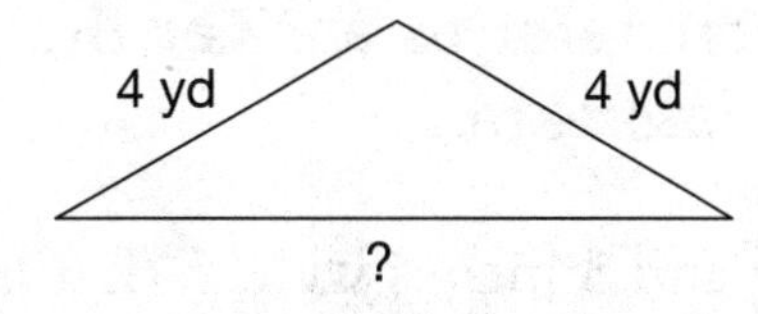

____

2. The length of one side of a square is 8 centimeters. What is the perimeter of the square?

____

3. The perimeter of the rectangle is 22 in. What is the length of the unknown side?

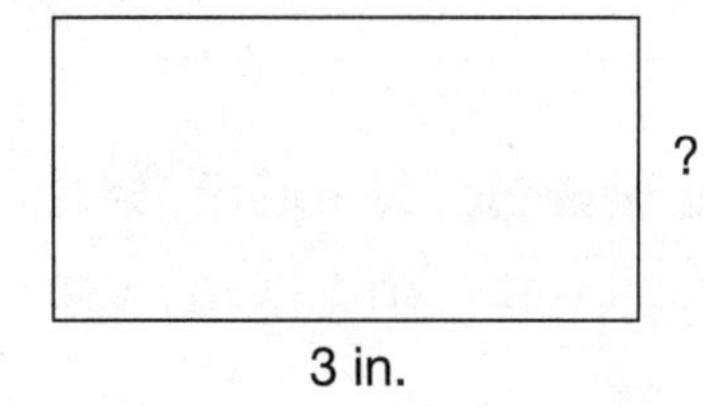

____

Put It Together

Find the perimeter of each figure. Show your work.

1.

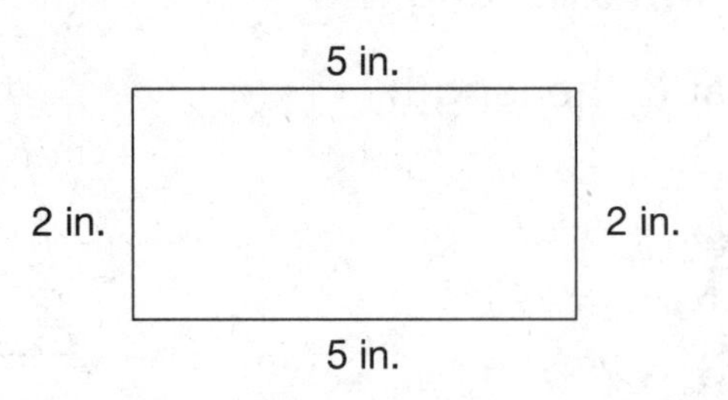

2.

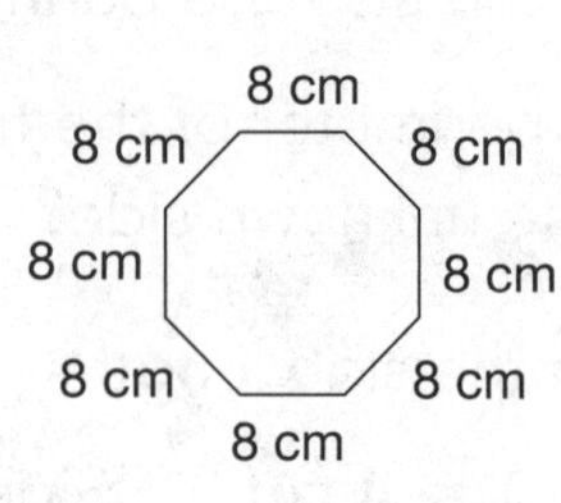

3.

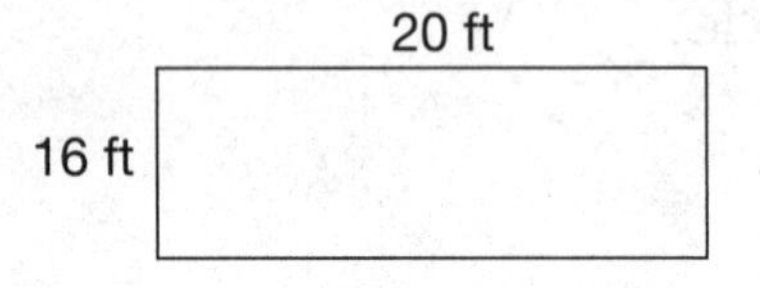

4.

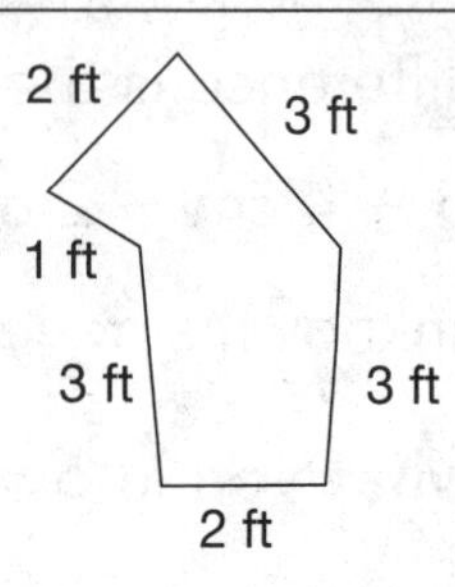

Use what you know about perimeter to answer the problems below. Share your solutions with a classmate.

5. A rectangle is 5 inches long and 3 inches wide. What is the perimeter of the rectangle?

6. The perimeter of the figure shown is 20 inches. What is the length of the unknown side?

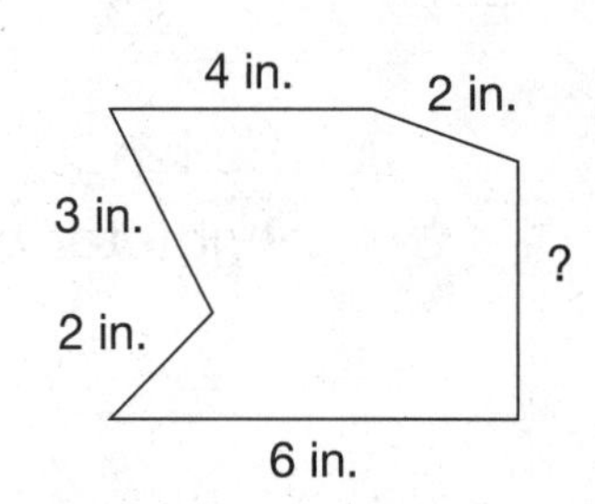

7. The perimeter of a square is 24 meters. What is the length of one side of the square?

8. Katie finds the perimeter of a triangle. Hope finds the perimeter of a rectangle. Compare and contrast the steps Katie and Hope use to find the perimeters.

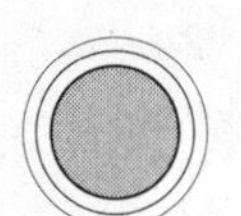

Make It Work

Answer the questions below.

1. What is the perimeter of the figure?

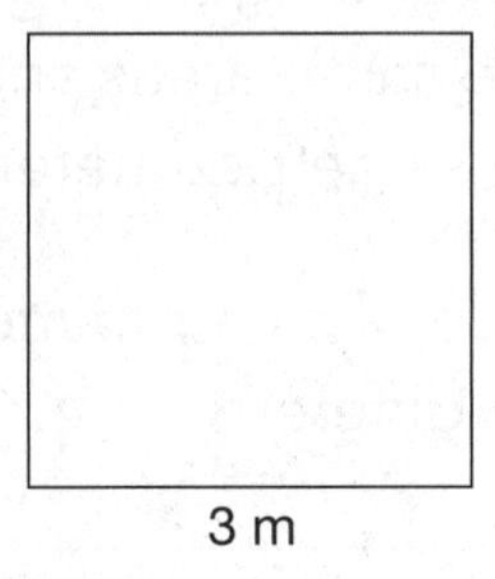

A. 6 meters

B. 9 meters

C. 12 meters

D. 15 meters

2. The perimeter of the figure is 22 m. What is the length of the unknown side?

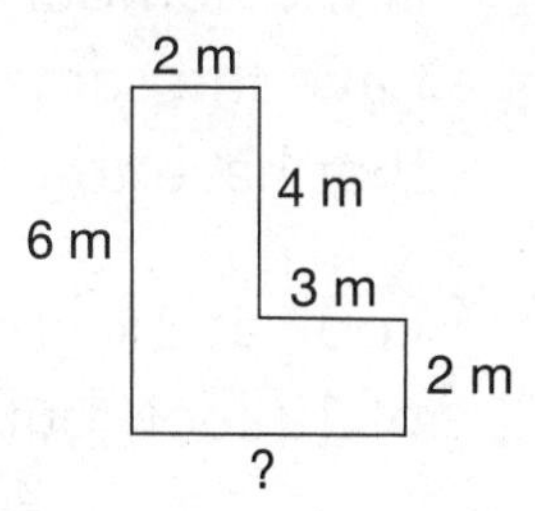

A. 5 m

B. 12 m

C. 17 m

D. 27 m

3. The sides of a triangle measure 3 in., 5 in., and 3 in. What is the perimeter of the triangle?

____

4. The perimeter of a hexagon is 42 cm. Each side of the hexagon is the same length. What is the length of one side of the hexagon?

____

5. Find the perimeter of three classroom objects you can measure using an inch ruler. Measure the sides to the nearest whole inch, and then use those measurements to find the perimeter. Record your results in the table below.

Object	Side Lengths (in inches)	Perimeter

Lesson 37 Perimeter and Area

3.MD.8 Solve real world and mathematical problems involving perimeters of polygons, including finding the perimeter given the side lengths, finding an unknown side length, and exhibiting rectangles with the same perimeter and different areas or with the same area and different perimeters.

Real World Connections

Toolbox
grid paper

You know that the distance around a figure is the perimeter and area is the number of square units needed to cover a figure. Figures that have the same perimeters may not have the same areas and figures that have the same areas may not have the same perimeters.

Look at the three gardens below. Each garden has a perimeter of 12 feet, but the areas of the gardens are different.

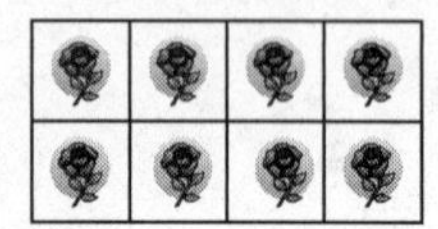	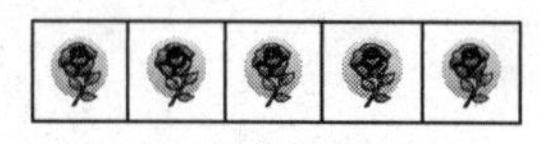	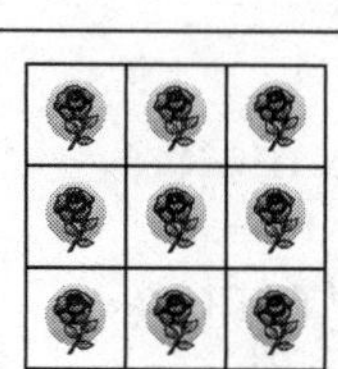
Perimeter $= 4 + 2 + 4 + 2$ $= 12$ feet	Perimeter $= 5 + 1 + 5 + 1$ $= 12$ feet	Perimeter $= 3 + 3 + 3 + 3$ $= 12$ feet
Area $= 4 \times 2 = 8$ square feet	Area $= 5 \times 1 = 5$ square feet	Area $= 3 \times 3 = 9$ square feet

Now look at the three rooms below. Each room has an area of 12 square meters, but the perimeters of the rooms are different.

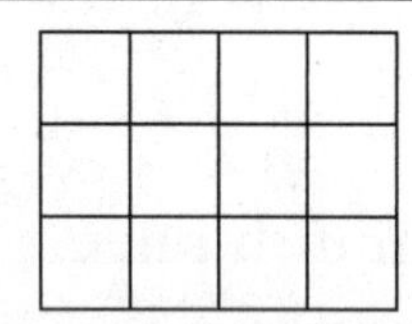	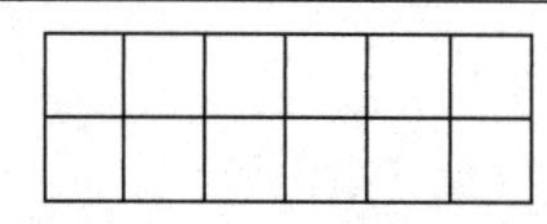	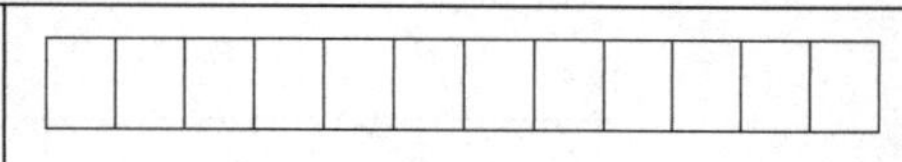
Perimeter $= 4 + 3 + 4 + 3$ $= 14$ meters	Perimeter $= 6 + 2 + 6 + 2$ $= 16$ meters	Perimeter $= 12 + 1 + 12 + 1$ $= 26$ meters
Area $= 4 \times 3 = 12$ square meters	Area $= 6 \times 2 = 12$ square meters	Area $= 12 \times 1 = 12$ square meters

Take It Apart

Carson has 8 feet of fencing. She wants to make a rectangle or square with the greatest possible area. What will the length and width be of the figure?

Step 1 Understand the problem. Carson has 8 feet of fencing, which means she can make a rectangle or square with a perimeter of 8 feet. You need to find the greatest area a rectangle or square can have with a perimeter of 8 feet.

Step 2 Use grid paper to draw rectangles and squares with perimeters of 8 feet.

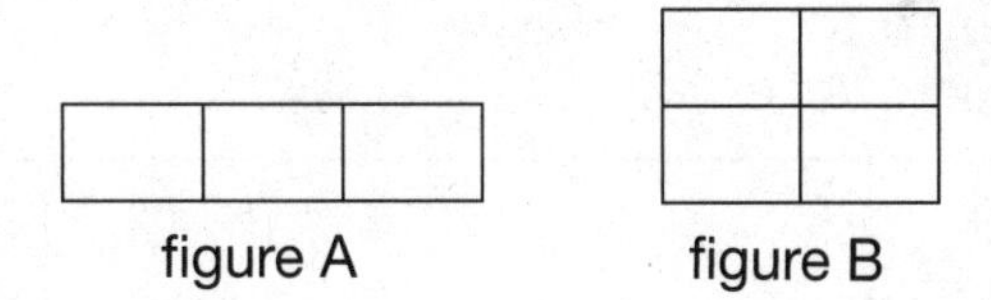

There are 2 figures you can draw that have a perimeter of 8 feet.

Step 3 Find the figure with the greater area.

Figure A has an area of 3 square feet.

Figure B has an area of 4 square feet.

Carson will make a figure that is 2 feet wide and 2 feet long.

Use what you know about perimeter and area to solve the following problems. Use grid paper when needed.

1. Mr. Larson has 10 yards of ribbon. He wants to use the ribbon to make a rectangle or square with the greatest possible area. What will the area of Mr. Larson's rectangle be?

____

2. The area of a rectangle is 16 square feet. What is the greatest perimeter the rectangle could have if the width of the rectangle is greater than 1 foot? Explain your answer.

____

____

Put It Together

Use what you know about perimeter and area to answer the problems below. Share your solutions with a classmate.

1. On the grid below, draw a rectangle with an area of 18 square units and a perimeter of 18 units.

2. Draw three different rectangles or squares. Each figure must have a perimeter of 20 units.

3. How many different rectangles can you make with a perimeter of 14 units? List the length and width of each.

4. Suppose there are two different rectangles. One figure has a greater perimeter than the other. Can you conclude that the figure with the greater perimeter also has the greater area? Explain.

5. Analyze how the area changes when rectangles with the same perimeter change from long and thin to square. Support your answer with an example.

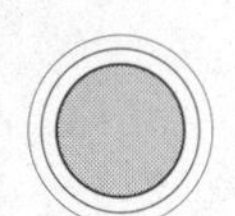

Make It Work

Answer the questions below.

1. Greta has 10 feet of ribbon. Which shows the rectangle with the largest area she can make with the ribbon?

A. 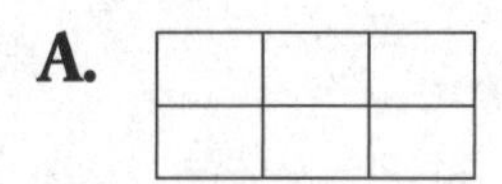

B.

C.

D.

2. Jim makes a rectangle with a perimeter of 18 inches. What is the greatest area his rectangle could have?

A. 14 square inches

B. 16 square inches

C. 20 square inches

D. 24 square inches

3. How many different rectangles can you make that have a perimeter of 16 units? List the length and width of each.

____

4. Trevor used 16 inches of wood to make a frame that had an area of 15 square inches. He wants to make a second frame using the same amount of wood, but wants it to have a greater area. What will be the length, width, and area of his second frame?

____

5. Draw three different rectangles on grid paper that all have a perimeter of 24 units. Record the length and width of each in the table below. Then calculate the area and write that in the table.

Rectangle	Length and Width	Area
Rectangle A		
Rectangle B		
Rectangle C		

Draw a conclusion about the shape of the rectangles compared to the area.

Kick It Up!

Chapter 4

Question 1: How can you describe your day using time?

Think of how often you use time each day. You use time to know when to get up, when school starts, when lunch begins, when school ends, and when to go to bed. Plus you use it for many other events during the day.

Work with a partner to describe your school day using time. You should discuss the daily activities and their start and end times. If your schedule varies from day to day, pick one day to use for the project. After you each finish writing the school schedule, then work independently to write your own before- and after-school schedules. Keep going until you have included all the major events in your day from waking up to going to bed.

You can continue the activity by making a chart showing the times for all of the major events in your day for a week. Compare the days to find what events stay the same from day to day and what events change.

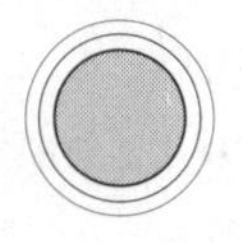

Question 2: When do you need to measure volume and mass?

In math class, you solve problems about volume and mass, but how will you use these skills when you get older? One way you will use volume and mass is when you are at the grocery store. Many foods are sold
by volume or mass and you need to understand these measures to make sure you get what you need.

Look at a grocery ad from the newspaper. Find the sizes of some products and use those sizes to write and solve word problems about volume and mass. For example, you may see that a 1 liter bottle of water is on sale for $1. If you need 5 liters of water, how much would that cost? Trade problems with a partner to solve.

If the grocery store ad does not list the sizes for some objects, use objects at home in your refrigerator and pantry.

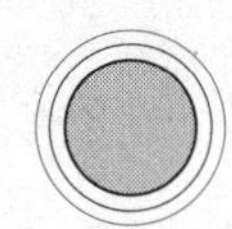

Question 3: When do you use graphs?

A great way to practice using graphs is to find graphs in newspapers, magazines, and books you read. Look through newspapers and magazines to find picture graphs or bar graphs to cut out. Two good places to look for graphs are in weather reports and in business sections. You can also look for bar graphs in your textbooks, too. But don't cut these out. Instead, make a copy of the graph and then cut that out.

Find at least 5 graphs. For each graph, write two questions that could be solved by looking at the graph. Then trade your graphs and questions with a partner. Have your partner use the graphs to answer the questions. Discuss the answers together.

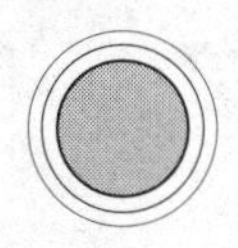

Question 4: How can you use a ruler to find perimeter and area?

Aren't you supposed to use square units to find area? How can you use a ruler to find area? You are about to find out.

Work with a partner to pick a rectangular object to measure using an inch ruler (so the object should be fairly small). Use the inch ruler to measure the length and width of the object to the nearest whole number. Use those measurements to find the perimeter and the area of the object.

Repeat the process for a total of 5 rectangular objects. Record the object, its length, width, perimeter, and area in a chart. Then compare the objects using the four different dimensions and compare the results. Order the objects from longest to shortest; widest to narrowest; greatest perimeter to least perimeter; and greatest area to least area. Does the order of the objects change each time? Is there any pattern to the objects? Draw conclusions about the different measurements with your partner.

Describing Polygons

3.G.1 Understand that shapes in different categories (e.g., rhombuses, rectangles, and others) may share attributes (e.g., having four sides), and that the shared attributes can define a larger category (i.e., quadrilaterals). Recognize rhombuses, rectangles, and squares and examples of quadrilaterals, and draw examples of quadrilaterals that do not belong to any of these subcategories.

Real World Connections

Toolbox

straightedge

Key Words

polygon
triangle
quadrilateral
pentagon
hexagon
octagon

There are shapes all around us. A **polygon** is a closed plane shape that has straight sides. Polygons are classified by the number of sides and angles they have.

Polygons		Not Polygons
triangle 3 sides 3 angles	**quadrilateral** 4 sides 4 angles	
pentagon 5 sides 5 angles	**hexagon** 6 sides 6 angles	
octagon 8 sides 8 angles		

Take It Apart

You can classify polygons by counting the number of sides.

How many sides does the polygon have? How can you classify the polygon?

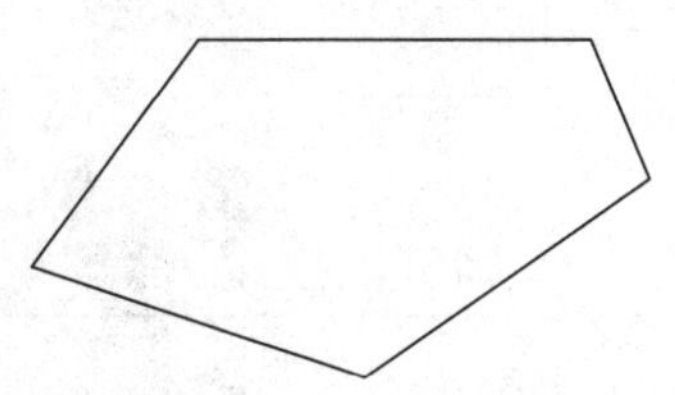

Step 1 Count the number of sides.

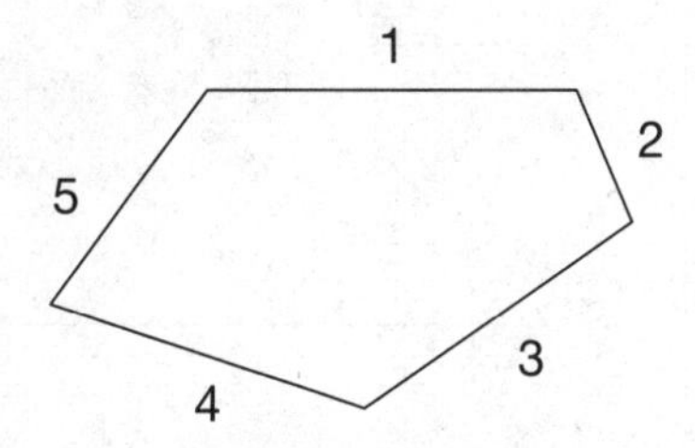

Step 2 Classify the polygon.

The polygon has 5 sides. So it is a pentagon.

Classify each polygon.

1. 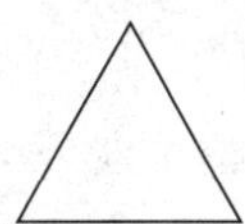

____

2. 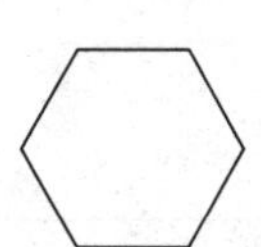

____

3. 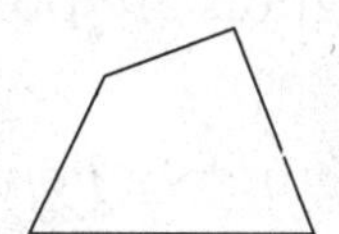

____

Use what you know about polygons to solve the following problems.

4. Dylan draws a polygon with 8 sides. What type of polygon does he draw?

____

5. Use a straightedge to draw a triangle.

Put It Together

Classify each polygon.

1. ______	2. ______	3. ______
4. ______	5. ______	6. ______

For questions 7–9, write the letters of the figures that answer each question.

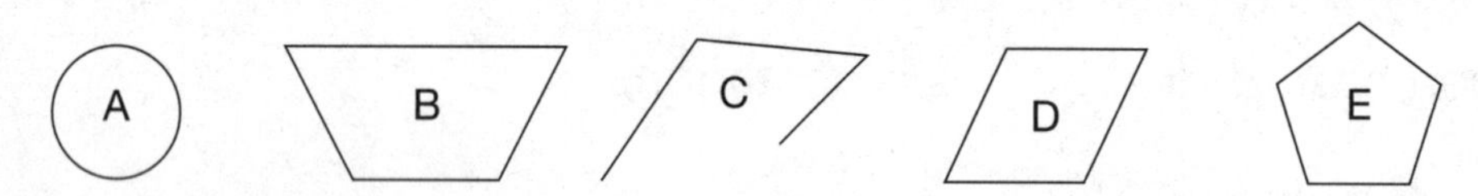

7. Which figures are polygons? ______

8. Which figure is a pentagon? ______

9. Which figures are quadrilaterals? ______

Use what you know about polygons to answer the problems below. Share your solutions with a classmate.

10. Solve the riddle: I have an even number of sides. I have more sides than a quadrilateral, but fewer sides than an octagon. What polygon am I?

______

11. A polygon has exactly 5 angles. How many sides does the polygon have? How can the polygon be classified?

______

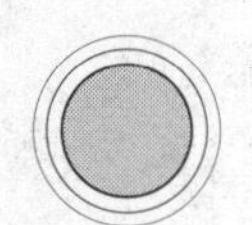

Make It Work

Answer the questions below.

1. Which figure is a pentagon?

A. 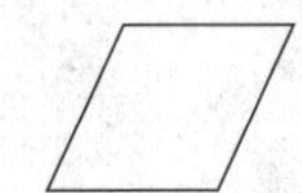

B. 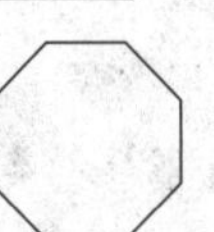

C. 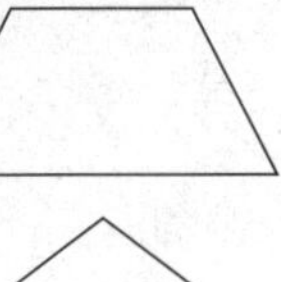

D. 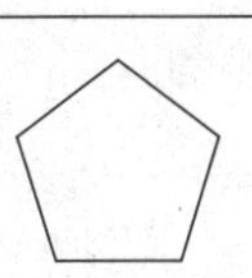

2. How many sides does a quadrilateral have?

A. 3

B. 4

C. 5

D. 6

3. While on the bus, Jessie sees a yield sign. The yield sign has 3 sides and 3 angles. What type of polygon is the yield sign?

____

4. Kevin draws a circle and says that his shape is a polygon. Is Kevin correct? If so, classify his polygon. If he is not correct, explain why.

____

____

5. Use your straightedge to draw polygons with 3, 4, 5, 6, and 8 sides. Classify each polygon.

____

____

Lesson 39 Classifying Quadrilaterals

3.G.1 Understand that shapes in different categories (e.g., rhombuses, rectangles, and others) may share attributes (e.g., having four sides), and that the shared attributes can define a larger category (i.e., quadrilaterals). Recognize rhombuses, rectangles, and squares and examples of quadrilaterals, and draw examples of quadrilaterals that do not belong to any of these subcategories.

Real World Connections

Key Words

- parallelogram
- rectangle
- square
- rhombus
- trapezoid

You learned in the last lesson that polygons with 4 sides and 4 angles are called quadrilaterals. Some quadrilaterals have special names.

Quadrilaterals with Special Names		Quadrilaterals without Special Names
parallelogram 2 pairs of parallel sides 2 pairs of equal sides	**rectangle** 2 pairs of parallel sides 2 pairs of equal sides 4 right angles	
square 2 pairs of parallel sides 4 equal sides 4 right angles	**rhombus** 2 pairs of parallel sides 4 equal sides	
trapezoid 1 pair of parallel sides		

Take It Apart

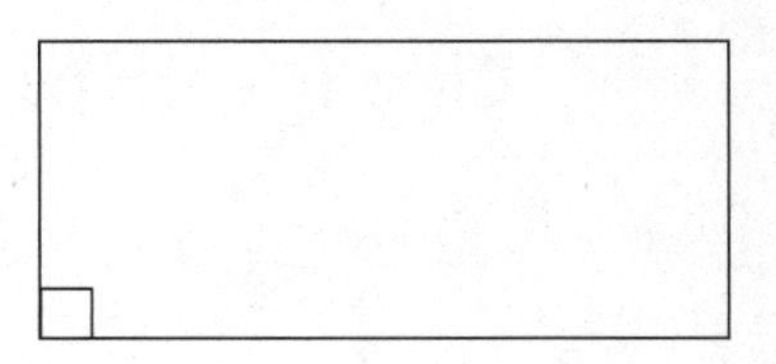

Classify the polygon in as many ways as possible.

Step 1 Classify the polygon using its sides. The polygon has 4 sides. It is a quadrilateral.

Step 2 Decide if it is a special polygon.

It has 2 pairs of parallel sides and 2 pairs of equal sides.

It is a parallelogram.

It also has 4 right angles.

It is a rectangle.

The polygon can be classified as a quadrilateral, a parallelogram, and a rectangle.

Classify each quadrilateral. Write all names that apply.

1. 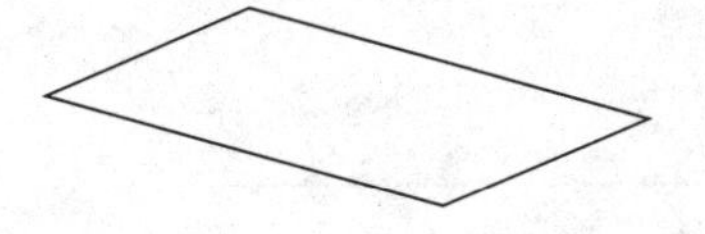

2. 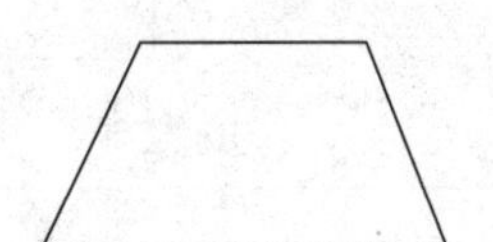

3. 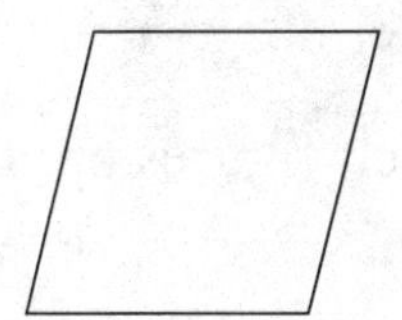

______________ ______________ ______________

Use what you know about polygons to solve the following problems.

4. Why are all rhombuses also parallelograms?

____

____

5. Henry draws a quadrilateral with 2 pairs of parallel sides and 4 right angles. The sides are all the same length. What quadrilateral did Henry draw?

____

Put It Together

Classify each polygon. Write the most specific name for each figure.

1.

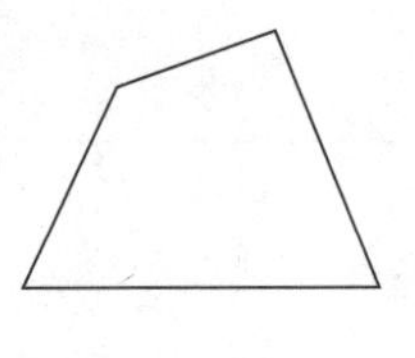

____

2.

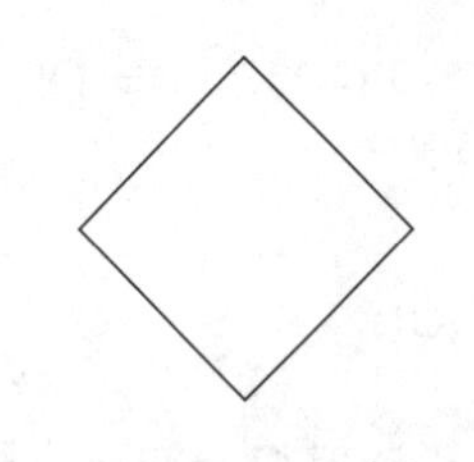

____

3.

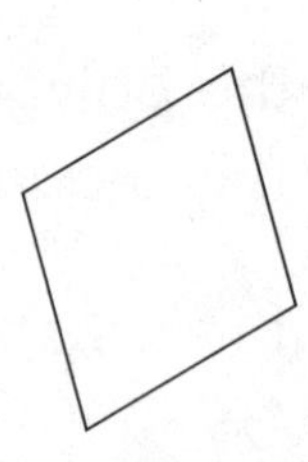

____

4.

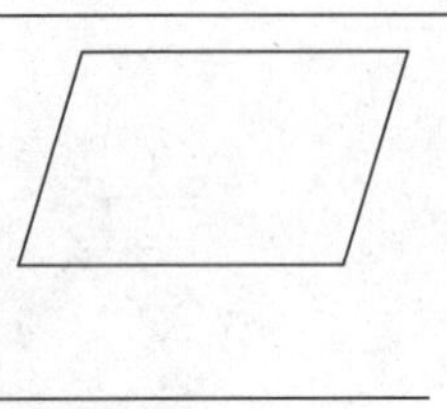

____

5.

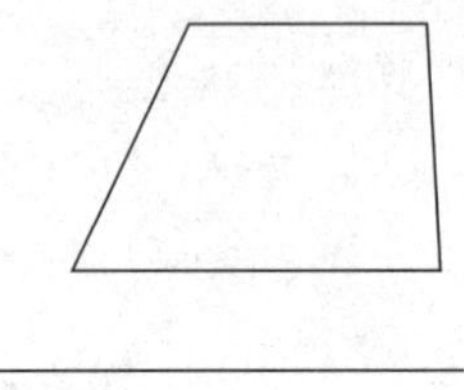

____

6.

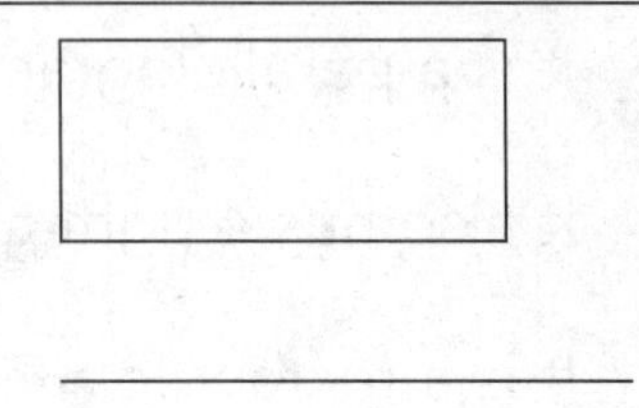

____

For questions 7–10, write the letters of the figures that answer each question.

A B C D

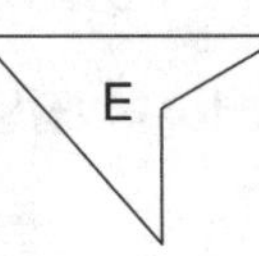

7. Which figures are quadrilaterals? ______________________

8. Which figures are parallelograms? ______________________

9. Which figure is a trapezoid? ______________________

10. Which figures are rhombuses? ______________________

Use what you know about quadrilaterals to answer the problems below. Share your solutions with a classmate.

11. Are all squares rectangles? Are all rectangles squares? Explain.

____

____

12. Can you classify a quadrilateral only by knowing its sides?

____

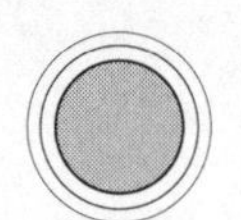

Make It Work

Answer the questions below.

1. Which figure has opposite sides that are parallel and no right angles?

A. 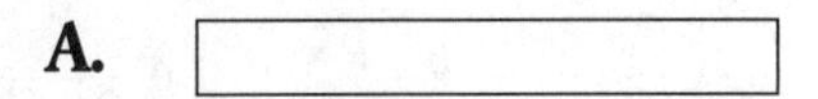

B. 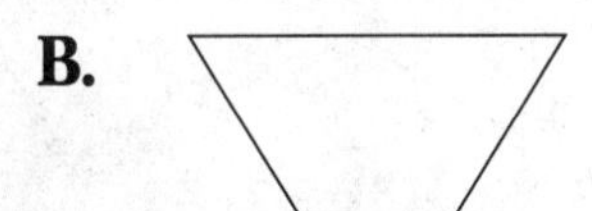

C. 

D. 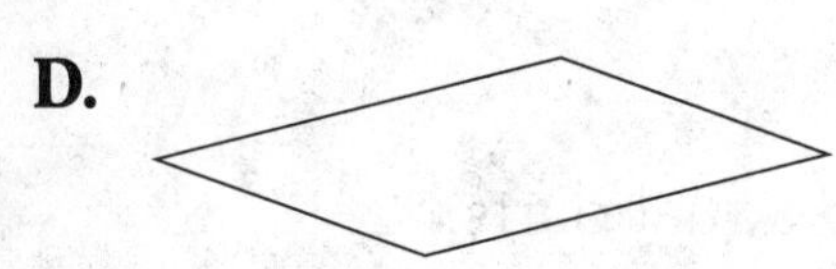

2. How many pairs of parallel sides does a trapezoid have?

A. 0

B. 1

C. 2

D. 3

3. How are a square and a rhombus alike? How are they different?

____

____

4. Sophie says that a square is always a rectangle, but a rectangle is not always a square. Is she correct? Explain why or why not.

____

____

____

5. Can a quadrilateral have sides that are different lengths and no parallel sides? Explain your answer and draw a picture to support your answer.

____

____

Dividing Shapes into Equal Parts

3.G.2 Partition shapes into parts with equal areas. Express the area of each part as a unit fraction of the whole. *For example, partition a shape into 4 parts with equal area, and describe the area of each part as $\frac{1}{4}$ of the area of the shape.*

Real World Connections

Key Words

- fourths
- halves
- thirds
- fifths
- sixths
- eighths
- fraction
- numerator
- denominator
- unit fraction

Jason helped his parents make a square-shaped pizza for dinner. They cut the pizza into 4 equal parts. There are different ways to cut the pizza into 4 equal parts.

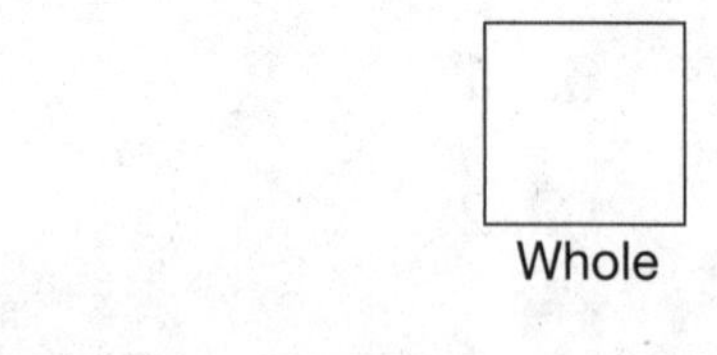

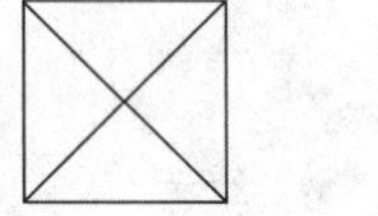 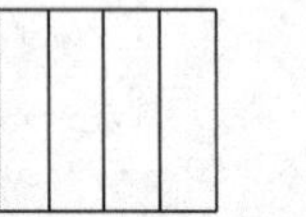 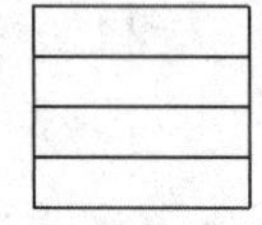 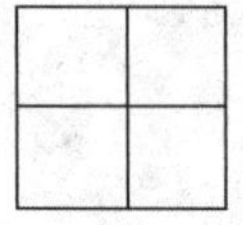

These pizzas are all divided into fourths. **Fourths** means that there are 4 equal parts.

There are other ways to divide a whole into equal parts.

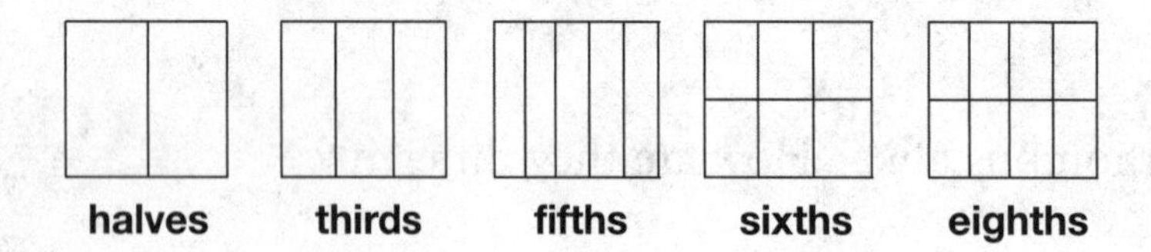

You can write a **fraction** to describe part of a whole. The **numerator** of a fraction tells how many parts are being counted. The **denominator** tells how many equal parts are in the whole.

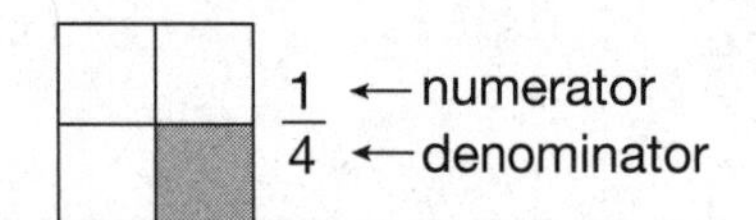

Say: "one fourth"

A **unit fraction** is a fraction that has a 1 as the numerator.

Take It Apart

Draw lines to divide the rectangle into thirds.
Shade 1 of the equal parts.
Write a fraction for the rectangle.

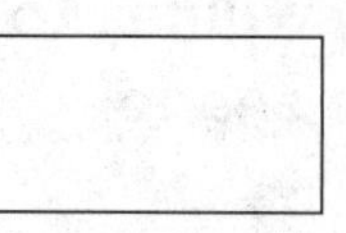

Step 1 Draw lines to divide the rectangle. Think: Thirds means 3 equal parts.

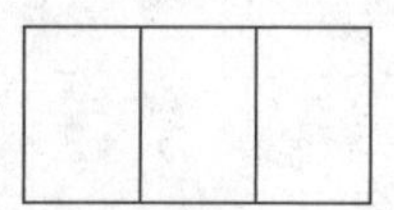

Step 2 Shade 1 part of the rectangle.

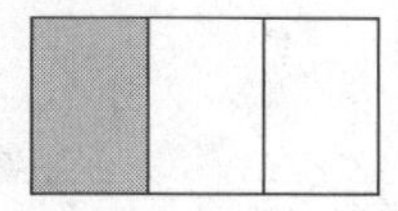

Step 3 Write a fraction for the rectangle.

$\frac{1}{3}$ ← number of shaded parts / ← total number of parts

Draw lines to show equal parts. Shade 1 part. Write a fraction for the shape.

1. halves

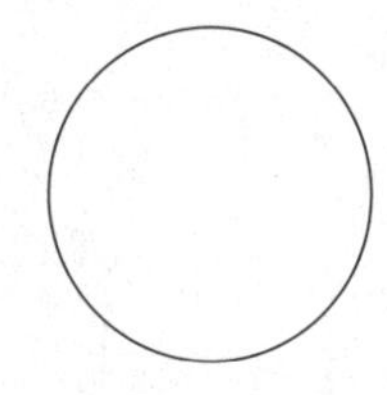

______

2. sixths

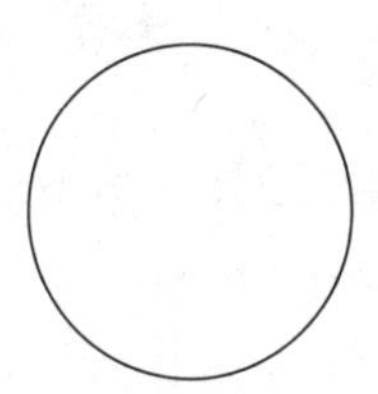

______

3. fifths

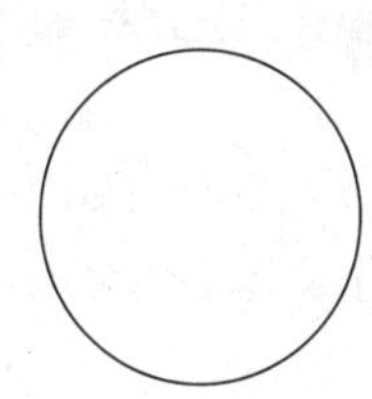

______

Use what you know about fractions to solve the following problem.

4. Circle the shape that is divided into equal parts. Write a fraction for that shape.

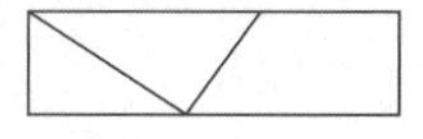 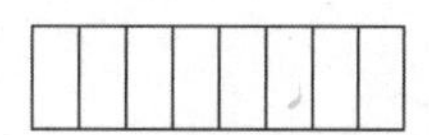 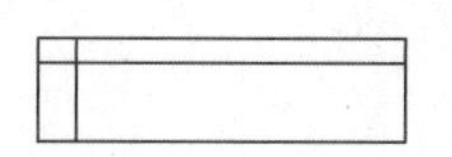 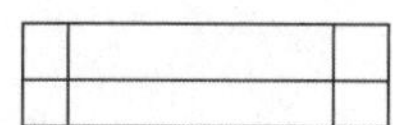

______

Put It Together

Draw lines to show equal parts. Shade 1 part. Write a fraction for the shape.

1. sixths

____

2. fourths

____

3. thirds

____

4. eighths

____

5. halves

____

6. fifths

____

Use what you know about fractions to answer the problems below. Share your solutions with a classmate.

7. Simon wrote the fraction $\frac{1}{3}$ for the triangle shown to the right. Explain why his fraction is incorrect.

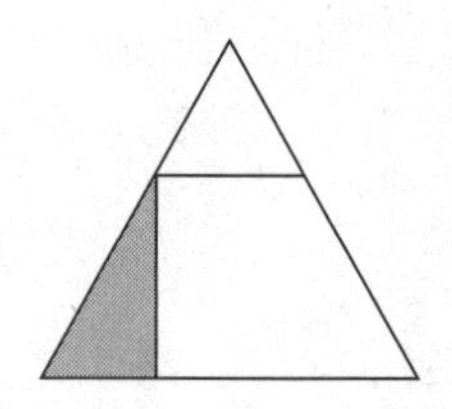

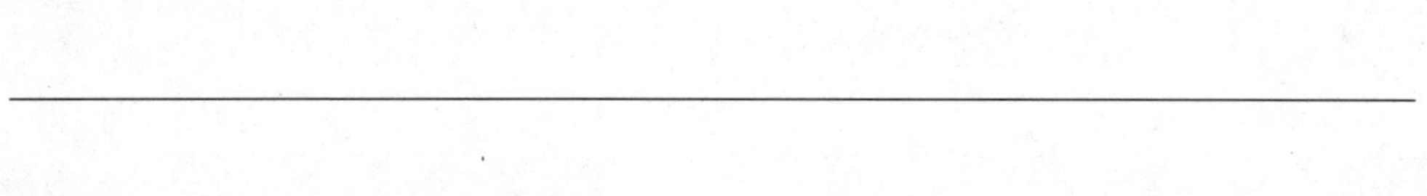

8. Complete the sentences using the figure to the right.

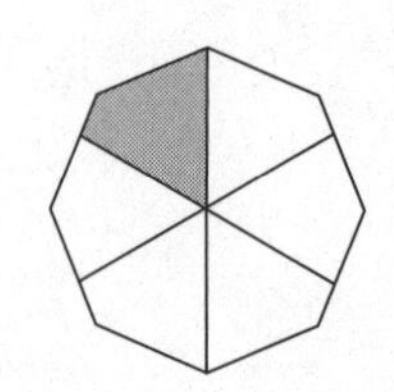

The figure is divided into _________.

It has _________ equal parts.

_________ part is shaded.

The fraction _________ describes the figure.

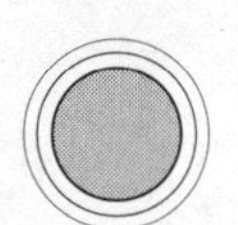

Make It Work

Answer the questions below.

1. Which figure shows one fifth shaded?

A. 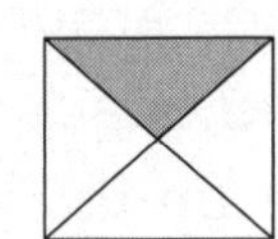

B. 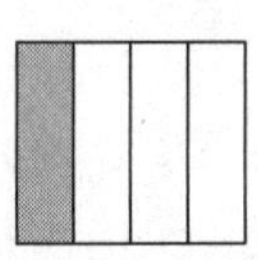

C. 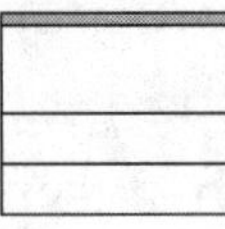 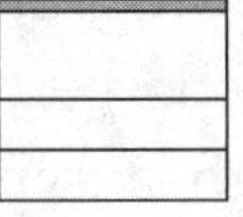

D. 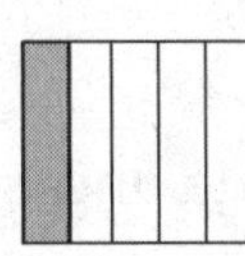

2. Which figure shows $\frac{1}{4}$?

A. 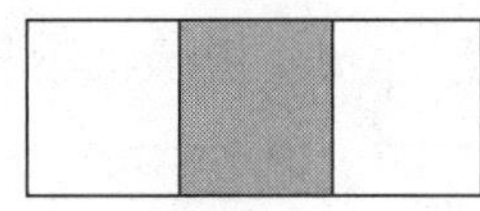

B. 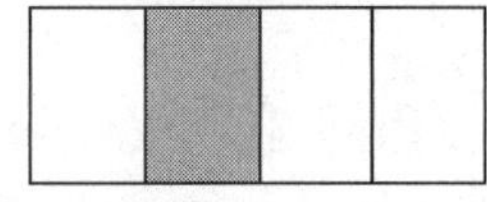

C. 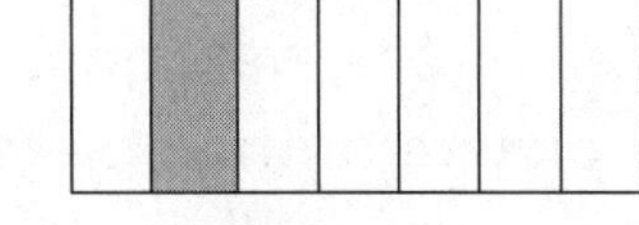

D. 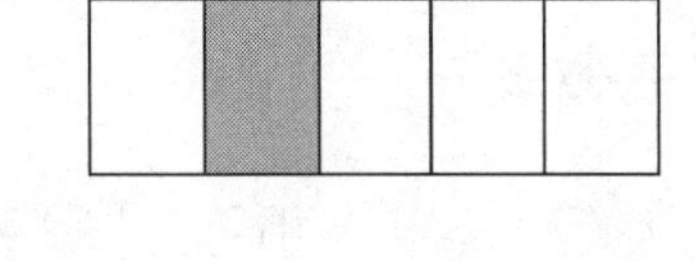

3. Draw lines to show eighths. Shade 1 part. Write a fraction for the rectangle.

____

4. Look at the figure to the right. Can you write a fraction for the shaded part? Explain why or why not.

____

5. Draw three identical shapes. Draw lines to divide the first shape into halves, the second shape into thirds, and the third shape into fourths. Shade 1 part of each shape and write a fraction for the shape. Then compare the shaded parts of the shapes. What do you notice about the size of the shaded parts compared to the denominators of the fractions?

____

____

Chapter 5

Question 1: Where can you find polygons?

Look around you. Do you see different polygons? Look at the board, at the bulletin boards, and in your backpack. Look around and try to find 5 quadrilaterals. Some objects that might be quadrilaterals: the cover of your spelling book, the board, a poster on the wall, a window, and a bookmark.

Try to find 10 examples of the polygons you learned about around your home or school. You will look for: triangles, quadrilaterals, pentagons, hexagons, and octagons. Take a photograph or draw a picture of the object. Label the polygon(s) in the picture. Make a booklet showing the examples you found, with one page for each polygon.

If you can't find 10 examples of a polygon, try making some of your own. For example, draw a hexagon in the sand or use rocks to show an octagon.

Question 2: How many different names can one thing have?

When someone asks you about your pet, you most likely would say more than "I have an animal." You would probably say what type of animal it is, its breed, whether it is a boy or a girl, and its color and name. In the same way, you can describe quadrilaterals with general names and specific names that give more information about them.

Work with a partner to develop a presentation that shows why some quadrilaterals have more than one name. Include in your presentation all of the different ways each quadrilateral can be named and show the connections between different quadrilaterals. Practice your presentation, and then share your presentation with some of your classmates.

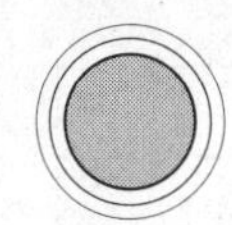

Question 3: What flags show equal parts?

Some countries have flags that are divided into equal parts. Research the flags of other countries using an almanac or the Internet (with an adult's permission) and find those that show equal parts. Create a poster of those flags. Label each flag with the country and how many equal parts the flag is divided into.

Share your results with a classmate. Discuss how the flags of different countries are all different. To extend the activity further, find out the meanings of different flags. Do the equal parts stand for something?

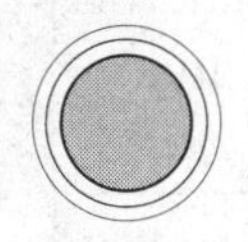

Question 4: When do you share using equal parts?

How often do you share an object? You may share a pizza with your family at dinner time, or split a sandwich in half with a friend at lunch time. You will probably be surprised by how often you share something using equal parts.

Brainstorm a list of things that you share using equal parts. Write five of those things in a tally table. For a certain period of time (a day, a week) make a tally mark any time you share using equal parts. Also write down what type of equal parts you used: halves, thirds, fourths, fifths, sixths, or eighths.

At the end of the experiment, review your results. What type of sharing do you do most often? Do you most often share with just one other person (halves) or many other people? Draw conclusions about sharing based on your data.

Rubric for Evaluating Math Assignments	
Points	**Criteria**
4	A 4-point response shows a thorough understanding of the essential mathematical concepts of the problem. The student executes procedures correctly and gives relevant responses to all parts of the task. The response contains a clear, effective explanation detailing how the problem was solved and why decisions were made. The response contains few minor errors, if any.
3	A 3-point response shows a nearly complete understanding of the problem's essential mathematical concepts. The student executes nearly all procedures and gives relevant responses to most parts of the task. The response may contain a correct numerical answer, but the required work is not provided or the response may contain minor errors.
2	A 2-point response shows limited understanding of the essential mathematical concepts of the problem. The response and procedures may be incomplete and/or may contain major errors. The explanation of how the problem was solved and why decisions were made may be confusing.
1	A 1-point response shows insufficient understanding of the problem's essential mathematical concepts. The procedures, if any, contain major errors. There may be no explanation of the solution or the reader is unable to understand how and why decisions were made.
0	A 0-point response is irrelevant, illegible, incomprehensible, or shows that no legitimate attempt was made to solve the problem.

TABLE 1. Common addition and subtraction situations.[6]

	Result Unknown	Change Unknown	Start Unknown
Add to	Two bunnies sat on the grass. Three more bunnies hopped there. How many bunnies are on the grass now? 2 + 3 = ?	Two bunnies were sitting on the grass. Some more bunnies hopped there. Then there were five bunnies. How many bunnies hopped over to the first two? 2 + ? = 5	Some bunnies were sitting on the grass. Three more bunnies hopped there. Then there were five bunnies. How many bunnies were on the grass before? ? + 3 = 5
Take from	Five apples were on the table. I ate two apples. How many apples are on the table now? 5 - 2 = ?	Five apples were on the table. I ate some apples. Then there were three apples. How many apples did I eat? 5 - ? = 3	Some apples were on the table. I ate two apples. Then there were three apples. How many apples were on the table before? ? - 2 = 3
	Total Unknown	**Addend Unknown**	**Both Addends Unknown[1]**
Put Together/ Take Apart[2]	Three red apples and two green apples are on the table. How many apples are on the table? 3 + 2 = ?	Five apples are on the table. Three are red and the rest are green. How many apples are green? 3 + ? = 5, 5 - 3 = ?	Grandma has five flowers. How many can she put in her red vase and how many in her blue vase? 5 = 0 + 5, 5 = 5 + 0 5 = 1 + 4, 5 = 4 + 1 5 = 2 + 3, 5 = 3 + 2
	Difference Unknown	**Bigger Unknown**	**Smaller Unknown**
Compare[3]	("How many more?" version): Lucy has two apples. Julie has five apples. How many more apples does Julie have than Lucy? ("How many fewer?" version): Lucy has two apples. Julie has five apples. How many fewer apples does Lucy have than Julie? 2 + ? = 5, 5 - 2 = ?	(Version with "more"): Julie has three more apples than Lucy. Lucy has two apples. How many apples does Julie have? (Version with "fewer"): Lucy has 3 fewer apples than Julie. Lucy has two apples. How many apples does Julie have? 2 + 3 = ?, 3 + 2 = ?	(Version with "more"): Julie has three more apples than Lucy. Julie has five apples. How many apples does Lucy have? (Version with "fewer"): Lucy has 3 fewer apples than Julie. Julie has five apples. How many apples does Lucy have? 5 - 3 = ?, ? + 3 = 5

[1]These take apart situations can be used to show all the decompositions of a given number. The associated equations, which have the total on the left of the equal sign, help children understand that the = sign does not always mean makes or results in but always does mean is the same number as.
[2]Either addend can be unknown, so there are three variations of these problem situations. Both Addends Unknown is a productive extension of this basic situation, especially for small numbers less than or equal to 10.
[3]For the Bigger Unknown or Smaller Unknown situations, one version directs the correct operation (the version using more for the bigger unknown and using less for the smaller unknown). The other versions are more difficult.

[6]Adapted from Box 2-4 of Mathematics Learning in Early Childhood, National Research Council (2009, pp. 32, 33).

Table 2. Common multiplication and division situations.[7]

	Unknown Product	Group Size Unknown ("How many in each group?" Division)	Number of Groups Unknown ("How many groups?" Division)
	$3 \times 6 = ?$	$3 \times ? = 18$, and $18 \div 3 = ?$	$? \times 6 = 18$, and $18 \div 6 = ?$
Equal Groups	There are 3 bags with 6 plums in each bag. How many plums are there in all? *Measurement example*. You need 3 lengths of string, each 6 inches long. How much string will you need altogether?	If 18 plums are shared equally into 3 bags, then how many plums will be in each bag? *Measurement example*. You have 18 inches of string, which you will cut into 3 equal pieces. How long will each piece of string be?	If 18 plums are to be packed 6 to a bag, then how many bags are needed? *Measurement example*. You have 18 inches of string, which you will cut into pieces that are 6 inches long. How many pieces of string will you have?
Arrays,[4] Area[5]	There are 3 rows of apples with 6 apples in each row. How many apples are there? *Area example*. What is the area of a 3 cm by 6 cm rectangle?	If 18 apples are arranged into 3 equal rows, how many apples will be in each row? *Area example*. A rectangle has area 18 square centimeters. If one side is 3 cm long, how long is a side next to it?	If 18 apples are arranged into equal rows of 6 apples, how many rows will there be? *Area example*. A rectangle has area 18 square centimeters. If one side is 6 cm long, how long is a side next to it?
Compare	A blue hat costs $6. A red hat costs 3 times as much as the blue hat. How much does the red hat cost? *Measurement example*. A rubber band is 6 cm long. How long will the rubber band be when it is stretched to be 3 times as long?	A red hat costs $18 and that is 3 times as much as a blue hat costs. How much does a blue hat cost? *Measurement example*. A rubber band is stretched to be 18 cm long and that is 3 times as long as it was at first. How long was the rubber band at first?	A red hat costs $18 and a blue hat costs $6. How many times as much does the red hat cost as the blue hat? *Measurement example*. A rubber band was 6 cm long at first. Now it is stretched to be 18 cm long. How many times as long is the rubber band now as it was at first?
General	$a \times b = ?$	$a \times ? = p$, and $p \div a = ?$	$? \times b = p$, and $p \div b = ?$

[4]The language in the array examples shows the easiest form of array problems. A harder form is to use the terms rows and columns: The apples in the grocery window are in 3 rows and 6 columns. How many apples are in there? Both forms are valuable.
[5]Area involves arrays of squares that have been pushed together so that there are no gaps or overlaps, so array problems include these especially important measurement situations.

[7]The first examples in each cell are examples of discrete things. These are easier for students and should be given before the measurement examples.

Table 3. The properties of operations. Here *a*, *b* and *c* stand for arbitrary numbers in a given number system. The properties of operations apply to the rational number system, the real number system, and the complex number system.

Associative property of addition	$(a + b) + c = a + (b + c)$
Commutative property of addition	$a + b = b + a$
Additive identity property of 0	$a + 0 = 0 + a = a$
Existence of additive inverses	For every a there exists $-a$ so that $a + (-a) = (-a) + a = 0$.
Associative property of multiplication	$(a \times b) \times c = a \times (b \times c)$
Commutative property of multiplication	$a \times b = b \times a$
Multiplicative identity property of 1	$a \times 1 = 1 \times a = a$
Existence of multiplicative inverses	For every $a \neq 0$ there exists $1/a$ so that $a \times 1/a = 1/a \times a = 1$.
Distributive property of multiplication over addition	$a \times (b + c) = a \times b + a \times c$

Table 4. The properties of equality. Here *a*, *b* and *c* stand for arbitrary numbers in the rational, real, or complex number systems.

Reflexive property of equality	$a = a$
Symmetric property of equality	If $a = b$, then $b = a$.
Transitive property of equality	If $a = b$ and $b = c$, then $a = c$.
Addition property of equality	If $a = b$, then $a + c = b + c$.
Subtraction property of equality	If $a = b$, then $a - c = b - c$.
Multiplication property of equality	If $a = b$, then $a \times c = b \times c$.
Division property of equality	If $a = b$ and $c \neq 0$, then $a \div c = b \div c$.
Substitution property of equality	If $a = b$, then b may be substituted for a in any expression containing a.

Table 5. The properties of inequality. Here *a*, *b* and *c* stand for arbitrary numbers in the rational or real number systems.

Exactly one of the following is true: $a < b$, $a = b$, $a > b$.
If $a > b$ and $b > c$ then $a > c$.
If $a > b$, then $b < a$.
If $a > b$, then $-a < -b$.
If $a > b$, then $a \pm c > b \pm c$.
If $a > b$ and $c > 0$, then $a \times c > b \times c$.
If $a > b$ and $c < 0$, then $a \times c < b \times c$.
If $a > b$ and $c > 0$, then $a \div c > b \div c$.
If $a > b$ and $c < 0$, then $a \div c < b \div c$.

Notes

Notes

Notes